CUBA'S MIRACLE LAD

And Other Missionary Stories

by

DON W. HILLIS

Home Secretary of the Evangelical Alliance Mission
as told to
Naomi A. Dallas

BAKER BOOK HOUSE
Grand Rapids 6, Michigan
1965

Library of Congress Catalog Card Number: 61-13671

First Printing, June 1961
Second Printing, April 1965

PHOTOLITHOPRINTED BY CUSHING - MALLOY, INC.
ANN ARBOR, MICHIGAN, UNITED STATES OF AMERICA
1965

A FEW WORDS TO THE READER

Ten of these missionary stories are based upon incidents which took place on mission fields, numbers: 1, 2, 4, 5, 7, 8, 9, 11, 12, and 14.

Three of the stories are based upon legend in India, numbers: 6, 10, and 13.

Two of the stories include true information about the missionary, numbers: 3 and 16; one story includes true information about the main character, number 1, and all three of these stories include missionary experiences typical of the lands in which they are laid.

The purpose of the book is to enrich the lives of young people in the Word of God, and to enlarge interest in missions.

Don Hillis

CONTENTS

Two stories in this book were rewritten and revised for book publication. Originally they appeared in the following publications and it is with their permission they are used:

"Biggest Goodness Ever"—as "I Might Have Hit an Angel," in Conservative Baptist Foreign Mission publications.

"Night Without Moon in Jungle"—as "The One-Eyed Animal" in Worldwide Evangelization Crusade.

Four stories are reprinted by permission from Child Evangelism magazine, "Biggest Goodness Ever," "Leopard Hunt for Suntosh," "Maddhu and the Tiger," and "Night Without Moon in Jungle."

1. CUBA'S MIRACLE LAD

"I want learning too! Very much I want learning!" Alfonso sobbed to himself as he leaned tight against his own little mud-brick house in Cuba. He could lean tight, too, for he was small and thin for a boy of eleven.

He peeked around the corner of the house every little while and looked toward the schoolhouse not far away.

Alfonso knew he probably looked as though he were playing a peek-a-boo game of some kind. For his face was almost covered with a big handkerchief and he peeked around a corner, then jumped back quickly if he saw any one.

But it wasn't a game Alfonso was playing. He was sad here all by himself, and he was thinking!

Alfonso touched a place on the not-very-clean handkerchief under which a cheek should have been. But the cloth covered only an empty place.

He touched the place where a chin should have been. But there was only a piece of chin there.

Under the cloth the boy opened and shut his mouth, but there were no lips to come together.

Alfonso peeked again toward the schoolhouse. He wanted to be there more than any place else in the world. Even with the boys and girls staring at him and whispering sometimes, he would be in the school every minute, even, if he could. Something inside him always cried out for great learning. And when he did get to go, he had better grades than any one else in the whole school!

But this morning the Roman Catholic Sisters, teachers in the school, had come to Mother and said Alfonso could not be in the school any more.

Alfonso was thinking about it as he stood by the house.

9

They say the bad disease on my face distresses the rest of the boys and girls!

The boys and girls had not always been distressed with Alfonso. Before his face was hurt and eaten away, when they played games they all wanted Alfonso on their side.

Then one day cousin Marcon came over to play. The two boys played and they ran. They had all kinds of big fun. Then Alfonso said, "Let me push you in my new swing, Marcos! I will push you so you go way up high to the tree limbs like the birds!"

Marcos asked, "High like the birds?" and his brown eyes were great big. Then he smiled with one side of his mouth and chewed his bottom lip on the other side.

Marcos sat down on the board seat in the swing and took hold of the rope on each side.

Alfonso went behind him and pushed. Up into the air went the swing with Marcos smiling now with both sides of his mouth.

Harder and harder Alfonso pushed. Higher and higher Marcos went. His toes touched the tree leaves before he came back, and he squeeled, "Ohhhhh!"

Then Alfonso quit pushing and dashed around in front to get a better look at the squeeling Marcos.

Alfonso didn't see Marcos at all. He didn't see anything! For, booopp, Marcos' feet hit Alfonso right in the face. Alfonso hit the ground, his feet in the air!

His face hurt! But Alfonso had been hurt before and this seemed not any worse. But in a few days the poisonous disease gangrene had set in.

Alfonso's family had heard about a doctor in another village. But many bad things were said about his doctoring people. So nothing was ever done about doctoring Alfonso.

The disease ate away at Alfonso's face. Soon a great piece was gone from his lower jaw. His lips were not lips at all any more. Only a bit of his nose remained.

10

Now because of his almost-gone face the Sisters would not let him come to the school anymore!

Alfonso peeked around the corner once more. The boys and girls were just going into the schoolhouse for classes. The boy wanted to run, to go in with them. He wanted to say, "I am *going* to have learning!"

A sob shook Alfonso's body. Then Mother's voice called, "Al-fon-so!" The boy jumped. He ran inside the one-room house.

Mother said, "Alfonso, sit down. I talk to you!"

Alfonso looked closely at Mother. A drawn, worried look was on her face.

Mother said, "Alfonso, I have decided! You go now to protestant school!"

Alfonso gasped. "Why Mother! That her-e-tic school! Ohhh, Mother!"

The boy watched Mother as she spoke again slowly, "I know Sisters and priest will be very angry. But you must have learning. You say your heart cries day and night for great learning!"

The inside of Alfonso's mouth was dry. He still had an inside to his mouth. His heart pounded. *It is a school!* he thought. He was too dazed to say words.

Mother looked very nervous. She twisted a corner of her big red-flowered apron. She said, "I know church Father, and Sisters at school will be very bad angry! But you must go, Alfonso. You must go!

Alfonso sat very still. He wondered if he would ever be able to move again. He felt fastened tight to the chair.

Mother spoke again. "When I went to protestant school to ask if they take you, the teacher said, 'Are you not afraid your church friends do bad things to you if Alfonso come here to school? Some families get stones throw at them because they no longer go to Catholic Church and they send boys and girls to school here!' Those teachers kind to me, Alfonso! I know it a good school. I can tell when I see

11

all things in the school rooms! And they will take you there, Alfonso! They will take you!"

Thoughts raced around in Alfonso's mind. *School! Learning! They will take me!*

Finally he said, "They *are* kind! Sometimes we throw dirt on their school steps. Sometimes we say bad names to them, the boys and girls from our school! But those protestant ones they never get bad cross with us. They just sweep off dirt. They smile and say kind like, 'Good morning boys and girls!' Funny people, those protestants!"

Alfonso's heart pounded wildly. Then he remembered something. Soon after his face was hurt, he was passing the protestant school and one of the teachers was on the path in front. She had looked at Alfonso and asked about his sore face. He had told her what happened and she said, "I'm sorry! I hope it will soon be better." She smiled and Alfonso was happy all that day from that smile.

Learning! You'll get great learning! something inside him was saying.

"I go, Mother! I go to that school! When people from Catholic school scold at me I say to them, 'You not want me! You should be happy I go away from your school!' "

Alfonso's mother did not smile, but a pleased look came on her face. Alfonso knew she was suffering for him. Suffering because of his very bad hurt, and because she knew how cross his friends would be with him now.

That very day Alfonso went to the protestant school. The boys and girls, there, were kind to him. Every one seemed happy in that school. They sang songs. They said prayers. A teacher even prayed right out loud for Alfonso. She prayed that his face would get well.

Face get well! Alfonso thought as the teacher stood praying. *I hardly have face any more! How can it ever get well?*

In school Alfonso studied as hard every day as if he had

12

been well and strong. He was one of the best students in this school too!

Then one day two of the protestant teachers came to Alfonso's home and talked with Alfonso and Father and Mother. The teachers said, "A Cuban Christian doctor would like to operate on Alfonso's face and help it to be much better!"

Operate! Alfonso thought. *I hear once that operate take all of family's money and all money they ever can get hold of for long time!* But Alfonso said no words. He only sat listening.

One of the teachers said again, "We have talked to the doctor about Alfonso wanting so much to have great learning and of his very good grades in school. The doctor says he will operate and it will not cost you any more money than you have that you can pay him."

Only what we can pay! Alfonso put his tongue to the places his lips should have been. His mouth was dry. His right hand twisted one finger after the other on his left hand. His eyes watched Father's every move, then Mother's.

Mother looked right at him asking without words, "Alfonso, you want operate or no operate?"

Alfonso ran to Mother and put an arm around her shoulder. "I will go fast for operate, Mother!" He looked at the teachers and said, "Oh thank you! So very much thank you! I go *now* with you for operate?"

The teachers looked at each other, and one said very kindly, "We'll talk to the doctor and see when he can take you, Alfonso. He is in the big village some miles away. But we shall make plans, and he will do all he can to make your face better!"

The next few days of waiting were long days for Alfonso. He could speak now only when cotton was packed in one side of his mouth. He could not work his jaw up and down; so he could not eat solid food. He had only liquids poured into his mouth from a tea pot.

13

Then came the day when the teachers took him and his mother to the hospital. Alfonso stayed for the operation.

This operation was followed by many more with Alfonso going home and to school sometimes between them.

His face was better. The bad disease finally was stopped. But the flesh that had been eaten away was forever gone.

One day the Cuban doctor talked to Antonio and Father and Mother about a Christian doctor in the United States who could help Alfonso's face even more. The Cuban doctor said, "The doctor in the United States can do another kind of operation called plastic surgery that will make Alfonso's face look almost like new."

Like new! Alfonso almost stopped breathing. *Did he say like new—or am I dream?*

The doctor's voice was kind as he spoke again, "It's sure to mean suffering! It will mean many months in the hospital there. Skin will have to be taken from other parts of Alfonso's body and be built in where the flesh is now gone."

Alfonso pushed the suffering part quickly out of his mind. "May I take books?" he asked, his heart happy. "If many months in hospital, much learning can I do there! O Mother, O Father, I go? I go to United States?"

"But how do we get money for trip way so far, and for operations by other doctor?" Mother's voice was low.

"She is willing! Is willing, my dear, good mother!" Alfonso said to himself. His eyes filled with tears and they spilled down onto his hollowed-out cheeks.

The doctor explained how Christian people in the United States give money to provide for care and for trips for people in need. He said they read in the Bible words the Lord Jesus said about doing good things for others.

The doctor opened a little Bible he took from his pocket and said, "Verses like this, I mean, '... Inasmuch as ye have done it unto one of the least of these my brethren, ye have done it unto me' (Matthew 25:40)."

14

So in a few days, in a sparkling clean hospital in the United States, Alfonso was seeing many of these good works being done.

Operation followed operation as month followed month. And every day Alfonso was hearing more from the Bible about the wonderful One, the Lord Jesus.

Alfonso studied hard from his school books. He studied too, from his very own Bible that the Christian doctor in Cuba gave him when he left there.

The day came for the last operation on Alfonso's face. As he lay looking up at the doctor he said, "Many months now have I heard about Lord Jesus who saves people from sin. Today I say to Him, 'Alfonso now take you for Savior!' "

Alfonso watched the doctor. His eyes were tender looking. The boy said again, "Lord Jesus, give Alfonso new life from sin! He give new face so no boys and girls ever be distress when I with them. I start now for study for be protestant pastor!"

The kind doctor said to Alfonso and to the nurses standing close by, "Let us pray, thanking God for this great day for Alfonso!"

It *was* a great day for Alfonso. It was the greatest day he had ever known in his life, for his heart was singing for joy that his sins were forgiven and that he now was a follower of the great living Christ. It was a miracle day too, for the last operation was the one that made Alfonso's face almost like new.

The long stay in the hospital was followed by long years of hard study. High school finally was finished. College years slipped by.

Then one day Alfonso who was now the principal of Cuba's largest seminary, sat behind his desk at the school. He tenderly picked up a page-worn Bible. Gently turning the pages he paused as he looked down into the book of Matthew. He began

15

reading softly to himself, ". . . Inasmuch as ye have done it unto one of the least of these . . . ."

A sob in the man's throat stopped his reading. But his eyes followed through the verse, "ye have done it unto me."

Alfonso's lips felt dry. He had lips! He moistened them with his tongue. "Thank you God!" he said. "I did so want a face!"

The man looked around the room at the books on the shelves. "And I did want great learning! Thank you!" he muttered. "O, thank you!"

Then words from another verse burst into Alfonso's mind, "He that winneth souls is wise" (Proverbs 11:30).

"Wise!" The man dropped his head between his two hands, his elbows on his desk. "O God, again thank you! For here at the school we win students to thee! So even above great learning from books, you have made *wise*!"

2. BIGGEST GOODNESS EVER

Keko trudged wearily along in the hot African sun on his way home from the village school. Thin and bony, he growled inside as he thought, *I learned the verse today, all right—"Oh how great is thy goodness...." I know it's true, the Bible is the great God's word! But I'd like to see some of that goodness from God!* Keko kicked the dust high in front of him.

Quickly the boy whirled himself around, ashamed of what he had thought. He felt almost as though someone had heard him say the words.

Then he saw Toki running toward him. "Help!" Toki was calling. "Get Bwana (African word for missionary or teacher) Trout to come quick and shoot buffalo! A whole herd is in the grain field!"

Bwana Trout, the white missionary, lived at the edge of the village.

We'll have no food if buffalo ruin grain, Keko thought as he dashed to the door and gave Bwana the message.

Charlie Trout, gun in hand, ran down the path toward the grain field. Keko was close behind. *Maybe I can do something too, to chase buffalo.*

Keko's thoughts raced as fast as he did. *Those big old fierce animals! Those mean ugly horns that curl up on each side of their heads!*

Keko kept following Bwana. *Buffalos always ready to hook somebody! And when they mad, oh-h-h-h, they more fiercer than worst jungle animals!*

Keko was right behind Bwana Trout when he reached Toki. By then the great beasts had edged into the jungle, too far out of sight for shooting.

"Gone!" said Bwana. "But unless we kill one of them, they'll come right back as soon as we leave. Once they've started eating in a grain field, they really have to be frightened to stay away."

Bwana thought for a minute. "Keko," he said, "you run back and get the three other missionaries and their guns. They can get up in these closest trees and be ready to shoot. We'll go around behind the buffalo and see if we can chase them this way. If we can, the missionaries won't have any trouble shooting one."

We'll go around behind the buffalo, echoed in Keko's heart as he dashed up the path. *He means me! He was looking straight at me when he said "we'll"!*

Keko and the missionaries were soon with Bwana and Toki. Bwana spoke quickly to the missionaries. "You get into the trees just inside the jungle. I'll take the boys and go around back of the herd. We'll try to move them this way. Shoot one if you can or they'll come back to the field as long as there's one thing to eat!"

The men moved toward the trees. Bwana looked toward the jungle, then at his wrist watch. He said to the boys, "One of you better not go with me after all. It's getting late. Someone must report to the village that we are after the buffalo."

Keko didn't move. He wanted to say that he wished to go hunt buffalo more than anything, but he knew that Bwana knew best.

Bwana looked from one boy to the other. "Keko, you are a little older and bigger—"

Keko's mouth was dry. He could hardly swallow.

"So, you go with me this time! Toki, you report to the village. Maybe next time you hunt buffalo!"

The boy turned and ran up the path toward the village. Bwana and Keko edged into the jungle.

Soon the two heard the animals not far from them. "I'll shoot into the air," Bwana said, "and scare them toward the

18

trees. If we shoot at them from here on the ground and wound one, he'll charge us!"

"Is right, Bwana, you shoot in air! We both shout! Then maybe animals run for grain field. Missionaries in trees can shoot! Can kill!"

Bwana shot into the air. The two shouted. Bwana shot again. Then again.

Keko touched Bwana's arm. "Buffalo not come this way if not wounded, will he?" Keko felt scared. He was ashamed, because he wanted to be brave and wanted to do something to help. *But buffalo are awful bad creatures!* he thought as he listened, breathless.

Bwana spoke, "No shooting from the trees yet, Keko. But listen!" The two looked at each other. "You know where those animals are going?"

"Into swamp!" Keko stood stunned.

"Sure as anything! Hear the slurp of that water!" Bwana said.

"Let's climb tree," Keko said, "and see for sure."

The two hurried up the tallest tree. "Bwana right!" Keko called from the branch he was on.

"Yes, and way out in the middle of the swamp now. They've outsmarted us, Keko. We may as well go back to the missionaries." Bwana said, as the two swung down the tree. They started back through the tall grass.

There was a movement in the grass behind them. They turned. A great hulk with horns curled up at the ends looked at them, then charged!

Bwana had time to fire only one shot. It missed the beast, but turned him into a mad creature. The next split second he had knocked Bwana down.

"What I do?" Keko screamed as he saw Bwana kick the great head. "I no gun! I no club!" The buffalo hooked and tossed at Bwana's feet.

I can pray, Keko thought. He squeezed his eyes tight shut

19

for a second. *The verse! Oh how great is thy goodness.*

"Please God show us thy goodness! Save Bwana Trout," Keko heard himself praying out loud.

A horn dug into Bwana's thigh.

"Please, God! Show us! Show us!"

The great head turned and the other horn caught Bwana under the knees and tossed him over his back. Bwana pushed himself up and staggered toward a tree. He stumbled over a rock and fell flat on his face. Keko screamed.

Bwana raised himself and tried to take aim at the animal. But the animal had turned around! It was moving away toward the swamp! Keko stood motionless. His mouth dropped open. He could hardly believe what he saw. He looked down at Bwana.

"Now I go fast for missionaries, carry you out, Bwana." Keko glanced toward the way of the buffalo. "He maybe come back! We get you out before he come back even more angry!"

Keko's breath was coming fast. "You keep gun ready, Bwana! You watch every direction!"

Keko dashed through the jungle. He stopped. *Voices!* he thought. *Yes! Voices!* "Who come?" he shouted.

"The missionaries," someone answered. "We saw a beast stray this way from the herd, then heard a shot."

Keko met the group in the tall grass. "Buffalo hurt Bwana, but not kill him!" he panted." Come fast! We carry him out!"

They rushed to Bwana and carried him out of the jungle. Keko kept close as they trudged up the path. *Now I see goodness of God,* he thought. *Now I see biggest goodness ever. I see God save life of Bwana Trout!*

Keko looked at Bwana, thinking, *I go fast tomorrow to tell teacher about it. I point to great God in heaven and say, Oh-h-h-h how GREAT is thy goodness!"*

3. NIGHT WITHOUT MOON IN JUNGLE

Kari (Ka rē') looked at Bwana Miller as though he must have said something he did not mean. The two were working on the right headlight of Bwana's car as the blackness of night without moon settled over the little village in the Belgian Congo.

"We quit?" Kari swallowed a great lump in his throat. "You mean we go on that dark jungle road with only one light? Oh-h-h Bwana!"

Kari was only twelve but he knew the jungle blackness. He knew that lions, hyenas, elephants and many other animals moved around in the dark.

"We sent word to the next village, Kari, that we would be there tonight," the missionary explained.

"But two headlights we all the time had till now, Bwana!" Another lump was coming in Kari's throat. And his breath was coming faster and faster.

"We told them it would be late before we got there. That we'd have our services here before we left," Bwana said. "So we must go, Kari! Remember, they'll have to have their services before they go to work in the morning so we'll need to be there."

Kari did not know if he could swallow at all or not. He was ashamed that he was so frightened. He thought, they must hear more about Lord Jesus too. I know we must go! But—

Kari looked carefully to see how far the one headlight shone down the road. He was motionless as he recalled the Bible verse they had said over and over in class one day, "Hear my voice, O God, in my prayer: preserve my life from fear of the enemy" (Psalm 64:1).

Are you listening, God? Kari leaned his head back and

21

looked into the lightless sky. *This is my prayer, Preserve my life from fear of the enemy, please. Amen.*

"Kari," Bwana Miller called to the boy.

Kari jumped as Bwana spoke.

"Do you still want to be the boy who goes on this trip or shall I get someone else, Kari?"

"O I go, Bwana! I go! I wait long time for my turn. Even with only one headlight and night without moon, I go! I go along!"

Kari and Bwana were soon on the road in the jungle. Kari sat forward on the edge of the seat carefully watching down the road. The one bouncy car light made wiggily, weird shadows in the roadway and close on each side. Kari kept looking straight ahead. "Don't you think pretty fast you drive for night when so little see?" Kari ventured. Then he added, "This is the most blackest night!"

Bwana answered gently, "I don't believe it's too fast, Kari. We want to get there as soon as we can."

They rolled up over a little knoll. "Are the windows all up good and tight, and the doors locked, Kari? We could be waylaid by wild animals. We don't want one coming in through a window. And we don't want one bumping a door handle and coming inside the car either!"

As they rode on, Kari climbed around and tested each window and made sure that each door was locked. He flopped back into his place to look again down the road.

They turned a bend in the road. Great shadows loomed up before them like tree trunks.

"Elephants, Bwana! Elephants!" Kari shrieked.

Bwana saw them too, but he was into the herd before he could stop. Huge wide faces and flapping ears seemed rushing right toward the two.

The car swerved one way. The car swerved another way, barely missing the tree-trunk legs.

Bwana jerked the car to a stop smack in front of a mother,

her baby moving back and forth by her with little short steps.

"Oh-h-h Bwana! We awful bad scare elephants too! They maybe never see noisy animal with one eye before on jungle road. Especially not in night without moon!" Kari was breathless. "That mother elephant, she mad, Bwana!" Kari leaned forward, his nose almost touching the windshield. "She getting madder and madder, Bwana! Look!"

The great animal pushed her front feet upward, swinging her trunk over the front of the car.

"Oh-h-h Bwana!" Kari jerked his head down to his knees and opened his hands wide on each side of his face.

"Crash!" came the trunk down on the good headlight.

Even with his head partly hid, Kari knew their only glimmer of light was gone!

"This is me again, God. Please preserve our lives from the fear of the enemy!"

The maddened elephant was ripping at the mud guards.

"What did you say about the enemy, Kari?" Bwana asked between noises.

"I was praying, Bwana. I didn't know I talking out loud!" Kari and Bwana had to yell at each other now to be heard.

"Riiipppppp!" went the tool box.

"She jerking off everything she can, Bwana. And once elephant start smashing it never quit till stuff flat on ground! What we do, Bwana?"

"There's only one thing we can do," Bwana Miller said. "Keep on praying! Remember Daniel in the lion's den!"

"Boom! Booooommmmmm!" the elephant's trunk beat again and again at the car. Then in a moment the car began to edge sideways.

"Oh, she right here on my side pushing!" Kari knew even in the blackness that only the side of the car was between him and the maddened beast.

"Squeek, scritch, thud, bump!" went the car as it was pushed along the road.

"We turn over, Bwana?"

The car stopped, upright! Then not one more sound except elephant's footsteps growing fainter and fainter. Then all was silent. Too silent!

Kari and Bwana sat hardly breathing in the dark. "We pray thank you and we think awhile, huh Bwana, while elephants get very far gone?"

"Yes, Kari, and I'm thinking of that little hurricane lamp that we carry."

"It here, Bwana! I see it when we work on headlight. It light, too. I push button then for see. I get it!"

Kari crawled over the seat into the back. He felt around until he found the lamp. Bwana was grinding away on the starter. "I fasten lamp on broken-good headlight, Bwana!" Kari got out with the lighted lamp and fastened it on to some dangling pieces.

The motor started. "Elephant not hurt engine, huh Bwana? We get on to village maybe?" The lump was in Kari's throat again.

The motor kept going. Bwana started the car down the road. The loose pieces banged and they bumped. The bent-together spots whined. But after a while the car crawled into the village and Kari and Bwana were telling their story.

"Sure now we know more and more of true God," a villager said, looking at one banged up spot on the car then another. "Great God He is to stop elephant! For mad elephant never stop smashing until damage is all done, is all done!"

Kari was glad for the spots of blackness there in the village. For he could step back into a shadowed place and feel alone with God. He moved a little way from the others. He said, "Thank you God that you hear my voice. Thank you for hearing prayer and preserving our lives from fear of the jungle enemies!"

24

4. CHING SURPRISES HIS FRIEND

Ching Ling listened to every word the grown-ups in his house were saying. They were all talking at once, neighbors who had come in, relatives, and people Ching did not know at all. They kept saying, "The Communists are coming!" Some said, "Can we hide?" Others, "We cannot go to other villages if Communists have roads block!" Still others said, "If we flee to hills what about sick who cannot go?"

Ching was thirteen, small, thin and black haired. He was so scared that inside he felt all jiggly. Outside his flesh felt cold and damp. And it seemed every hair on his head was standing out in a different direction.

Ching thought, *O! What about Missionary Preedy? First thing Communists sure capture missionary! He my very best friend besides Father and Mother!* The boy didn't move. He just kept on thinking. *Missionary Preedy must not be take away from Ching's village! How could I live without good friend very close? I quick go and tell!*

Ching looked for Father and Mother. He pushed his way between people looking, looking! *Where are Father and Mother? Too much crowd people, can't find! Ching pushed a swallow down his dry throat. They would want I go tell! I go!*

Ching slipped through the crowd and out of the door. He ran down the narrow winding streets. Ching ran very fast.

As Ching ran, thoughts ran through his mind. *Father and Mother even accept missionary's new Jesus God. I love missionary Preedy! I sometimes not want to come home from his house. But this Jesus one—I don't yet know about him! I thinking though! And while I thinking I still go to temple and take sacrifice to gods!*

At the missionary's house Ching did not knock. He pushed

25

open the door. He called, "The Communists coming, Mr. Preedy!"

Clarence Preedy stepped in from another room as words tumbled out of Ching. "Big crowd to our house all together talking about Communists! You hide, Mr. Preedy? You go to mountains? You try get to coast, sail away?" Questions and questions came out of Ching.

The missionary stood still, Ching now close beside him. "Let's pray, Ching! Let's ask God to show us what to do!" the man said quietly. A strong arm reached around a thin shoulder and held it close.

"*You* pray, Mr. Preedy! Ching, he just listen! Ching give sacrifice to gods in temple, not want to make angry talking to missionary's God!" Ching closed his eyes.

Chester Preedy prayed for guidance for everyone in the province. He prayed for the Communists, that their hearts would be changed from hate for God to love for Him.

That one prayer that not get answered, Ching thought. *Not those Communists! They never love nobody nor nothing!* Ching thought of many kindnesses he had seen the missionary do for people who sometimes were not even friendly. *Missionary so much good friend to just everybody!* Ching thought.

When Mr. Preedy finished praying Ching looked up at him. "I go quick home now! I like longer stay but I go back now. Good night Mr. Preedy!"

"I'll go back with you, Ching, so you are not alone!" the missionary said.

Ching answered, "No, you stay your home! Ching go alone fast, very fast! Alone, slip from shadow to shadow if hear Communists right in village." The boy stepped into the night and was gone.

Ching barely was started when a great burst of fire lighted the sky just outside the village. "Boom! Crack! Bang!" sounded beyond in the streaking light.

Ching said to himself as he ran, "Those mean bad Commun-

26

ists! They come into village, kill people! Carry villagers away, never let come back! They mean worser people than anybody on earth!"

As Ching neared his home he saw the crowd outside that had been inside when he left. Now everybody was talking even faster. Ching looked for Father and Mother. Some of the people were pointing toward the fire and great booming noises.

The fire grew bigger and bigger and the noises so loud Ching put his fingers into his ears. With his elbows close to his sides he shouldered through the growing crowd. "There's Father and Mother!" Ching pushed to them.

Mother said, "Ching, we uneasy for you! Long time not see you! Father and I go alone and pray great God in heaven be taking care of you!"

Ching answered, "I go fast and tell missionary about Communists coming!"

"O Ching, thank you!" Mother said. She looked with a sad kind look into Ching's eyes. "Now stay close by Father and me. Maybe Communists come into village before morning!"

Ching grew so weary he asked Mother about going to bed.

"We go inside and find mats then!" Mother answered. "Many people will be sleep in our house. Great living God give us much big house. We share with people who have much fear. They not trusting in living God! They want be with us!"

Inside, many people were already sleeping on the floors. Ching lay down on a mat, not sleepy now at all as he was out of doors. He began thinking and thinking.

He thought about the gods he took rice to today in the temple. *He not even blinking eyes or nod head,* Ching remembered. *But I see him. And God missionary tell is living God who is everywhere all time. I not even see!*

Ching's thoughts were chasing each other as he dropped off to sleep.

He slept so hard and so long that when he awakened only a

few people were still in the house. Mother was sitting on the floor near Ching.

"Not Communists last night after all, Ching!" Mother said. "Fire and great noise, big ammunition dump getting start burning!"

Ching saw Mother twist her small white hands as she talked. Her face was extra pale. It was very sad looking. Ching opened his mouth to ask something when Mother added, "This morning very bad news! Moslem governor of our province fly away in great American airplane he rent. He take much gold! Many women to entertain! He go to safety and leave province without ruler!"

Ching's mouth dropped open. His eyes looked straight into Mother's. "Without ruler! Then there is big lawlessness all over province! There is stealing and trouble!" Ching had grown up hearing of villages where there was no law and no order.

"Yes!" Mother nodded her head sadly. "There already now shooting in our own village! We have been warn, 'Do not go out of house!' Much smashing of windows and stealing from stores is going on in business part!"

Mother turned quickly and looked toward the window. She was listening! Ching could tell she was listening carefully! Then he heard it too!

"Horsemen, Mother! Many horsemen!" Ching said. He edged over tight against Mother.

"Yes, Ching, many horsemen!" Mother sort of breathed the words into Ching's ear.

" Look, Mother!" Ching pointed through the window. "They galloping through the streets! Are they Communists, Mother, Communists?" Ching was shaking from the end of his longest black hair to the tip of his smallest two toes.

The horsemen left as mysteriously as they had come. All was quiet in the village then the rest of the day.

Several days passed with only uneasiness. Each day Missionary Preedy slipped over to Ching's house or Ching went quickly to Mr. Preedy's.

Sometimes rumors would arise that help was coming from other provinces where there were still good rulers. If help were to come when the Communists arrived, they could maybe be driven back. Some mornings, from out of the no-where, great pasted-on slogans would give forth messages from walls high on buildings. The slogans always bore welcomings of one kind or another to the Communists! No one could learn who put them up.

One day when Ching was at the missionary's house, there was shouting and clapping and great sounds of "welcome" out in the streets. Ching and Mr. Preedy stepped out-of-doors.

Truck loads and truck loads of well-dressed men were driving through the great city gates.

Ching blinked. He twisted his head one way then another to watch the men.

"Communists!" Mr. Preedy whispered.

"Communists! No!" Ching whispered back. "People are saying 'Welcome!' It can't be Communists, Mr. Preedy!"

"Those people clapping and saying 'Welcome' believe the black lies of the Communists, Ching," the missionary said. "They will be fooled for a while by the promises and tricks of these Godless men!"

The people in Ching's village *were* fooled for a long time. With the governor of the province gone, the Communists acted as rulers. They put down the lawlessness that had been going on since the governor left. Thy acted as though they were giving the people real security. They called themselves the "Liberation Army."

The soldiers acted orderly. When they went into homes and quietly took whatever they wanted, they even sometimes returned the things so the people would not feel they were so bad after all.

The Communists worked so smilingly and so wisely that they

29

had no trouble at all staying in the village. The people who lived there went about their regular work and the Communists only smiled bigger and bigger at them.

Then at the end of a year, the Communists took over the government control of the city without anyone telling them they could.

They made up bad stories about people in the village, which was really almost a city, and would have them tried in their Communist courts. Usually they had them very severely punished. Sometimes the punishment was sending them far away where they could never return to their families.

Ching's family lived from day to day in fear they would be next in the sudden arrests. Each day Father would say, "Great living God in heaven will be with family! If we get separate, He will still be with us. If we get kill we go to heaven to be with Lord Jesus who save us from sin!"

Ching looked straight into Father's face. It was sad and drawn, but it was peaceful looking. Ching knew that his own had no look of peace on it. Thoughts were tumbling around in his mind. *Die! Go to heaven! The god in temple make no promise of heaven!*

Ching felt sick in his stomach as he remembered the great mass killings the Communists were doing these days.

One day a thunderous knock on the door came and Ching and Father and Mother all looked up. The door opened and there stood the dreaded men in gray exactly as the family had heard they were apt to do.

No one spoke a word. The men moved from cupboard to drawer, looking, looking! One lifted the lid of the cookie jar and peered in. One sniffed of the bottles of spices.

They sprawled into the easy chairs and picked up the National Geographic books Mr. Preedy had given Ching to look at.

Then men in gray looked through the books. They held up

30

pictures to each other, and smiled and said things real fast that Ching could not understand.

Ching wondered if they were going to stay in their house! He wondered if they would take Father, or maybe Mother, along with them. *They maybe take me!* something suddenly said inside him. *I wonder what Mr. Preedy right now be doing. Maybe Communists take him away!*

The Communists took themselves out of the house as suddenly as they had come in. As rulers of the city, they forced people to listen to studies of Communism telling what good they were doing wherever they were! Loud speakers blared forth in the streets things that sounded wonderful, lovely! *Do they think we have no brains for thinking for selves?* Ching thought one day as he listened. Then Ching wrinkled his forehead. *Thinking for self! Thinking! For self!* Ching remembered how he had dashed into the temple that morning, mumbled some words to the god there and dashed out again without any real thinking.

I go again and talk with missionary friend about living one Lord Jesus, Ching decided.

So Ching arrived at the missionary's house in a few minutes. The front door stood a little way open. Ching knocked. He called. He looked inside the door.

"Is gone! Mr. Preedy and some of the furniture, gone!" Ching heard himself talking. "He tell me all but four of missionaries already leave province! Those four refuse go. They stay with Chinese friends bossed by very bad Communists!"

Ching looked closely at everything in the house he could see without going one step inside. He knew the furnishings there as well as he did in his own home. "He not go because he want!" Ching said, looking at some books open on the floor, pages walked on and ripped loose.

Ching turned and ran to his own home. He told Father and Mother, "Mr. Preedy is gone! The Communists take Mr.

Preedy, spoil his books!   O, our friend, our good friend Mr. Preedy!"

Father and Mother and Ching all looked at each other. Father said, "We very much pray living God in heaven for missionary."   Father and Mother prayed.   Ching listened.

Ching wished he could look at Mr. Preedy.   He wished he could talk with his friend.   He wished Mr. Preedy could talk with him.

Then one day a post card came in the mail from the missionary.   It told that he and the three other missionaries were each in a different place.   They could not see each other, but they could write if they used cards.

"I know!" Ching said.   "Those Communists have to read every word!   But O, so good to hear from good friend.   Only wish Ching could see!"

Sometime after that the missionaries *were* where Ching could see!   They were taken into public gatherings and there before the people they were made fun of!   They were asked all kinds of questions about things they knew nothing of.

After two years and three months, Ching heard a certain knock at the door one day. He jumped. *That knock!* he thought. His heart pounded as he ran to open the door. "Mr. Preedy!" Ching could hardly speak his friend's name.   Then words began to come freely.   "I knew it your knock, Mr. Preedy!   Come in! Come fast in!"

There was much talking soon with Father and Mother and Ching all asking Mr. Preedy questions.

Once he answered, "No, we did not have to work hard. Much of the time we did not have enough work to do.   They let us only sit or lie down with nothing at all to do!   O, how we did want to be working again!"

Another time he said, "Yes, we were lonely!   We were very lonely!   But we had the Lord Jesus in our hearts and we would talk with Him.   We would sing softly.   We would say verses of Scripture.   Though we missionaries were not together, we all did the same things to pass the time away! So even while we were lonely we had happiness in our hearts!"

Ching was watching every move of the missionary. He saw happiness even in the thin drawn look on the friend's face.

Mr. Preedy looked tenderly at each of the people before him. He said, "I am very sorry this is my last time to be with you. We have been given orders from our own government that we must leave at once and not come back into China! I am only grateful to God that He made it possible for me to come to you today!"

Mr. Preedy stood up to leave. Ching hastened to his side. Ching said, "Mr. Preedy, Ching have very big surprise for you! This time when you go away, you not really go way from Ching after all! I too accept your living Jesus God, and you remember you read me one day, 'We are one in Christ Jesus!' "

Ching watched his friend closely. He looked too at Father and Mother. They both had tears in their eyes, but there were smiles on their faces. Mr. Preedy looked at Ching and Father and Mother.

Ching added, "You very far go to United States, Mr. Preedy! You may not ever come more to China. But you God's man, Mr. Preedy and you go always where God say, not where Mr. Preedy say!"

The missionary put an arm around the boy. Ching added, "Our hearts and Mr. Preedy's heart all time be one together! All loving same God, Lord Jesus. Good-by, Mr. Preedy!"

The missionary shook hands with his Chinese friends, and walked slowly out the door. Dampness from Ching's eyes dripped onto his shirt as he watched his friend from the window. He thought to himself, *So glad Ching now too belonging to great living God. Is now always together with Mr. Preedy and parents, no matter what Coommunists do. For in great one Lord Jesus there is never no separate!*

5. KOH AND HIS BAMBOO BANK

Koh (Ko) sat on the dirt floor in the little mud and stone church on an island southwest of Formosa. Everybody was singing, "Jesus loves me this I know, for the Bible tells me so." Everyone there loved to sing that song because everyone in the little church loved the Lord Jesus.

Those grown-ups! Too soft they sing! Koh thought. *I love the Lord Jesus and loud I want to sing for Him!* So Koh opened his mouth wide and sang and sang!

Then the native pastor began to speak. He talked of the God in heaven who is a living God. Koh thought, *He not like the piece of fish skin with no eyes, with no ears that Koh and Father and Mother USED to pray to!*

A native evangelist had gone to the little fishing village two years before and had told about the living God who can take away sin. All of Koh's family and many other villagers had believed the good news and had accepted this One, the Lord Jesus.

The people listened as the pastor talked about the new little church they had built where they could come to worship.

Koh listened. Then he became sad as the pastor said there was no money to buy wood to make benches for the church.

"I wish I could help get money," Koh said to himself. "We very much need benches for sit!"

Then the pastor said, "Everyone is going to get to help bring money for benches! Even boys and girls can help!"

Koh wrinkled his forehead. *Did the pastor say what I think he said?* he wondered. Koh sat up straight and tall-like. Someone began passing out short pieces of bamboo poles with money slots cut in the sides. The bamboos were cut at the joints so

34

each was sealed tight at both ends. And sure enough, boys and girls were getting them too!

"Bamboo banks!" Koh said to himself as his fingers closed on the slick hard piece of bamboo that was to be his. His heart began to beat faster. "But where I get money to put in bank? Nobody hire eleven-year-old boy!" he added biting his bottom lip.

Koh started to hand back his bank. Then he looked at the people sitting on the dirt floor. "The house of living God must have wood benches," he said under his breath. "Some way I help too!"

Next morning Koh wandered down to the shore to watch the fishermen catching fish in their big nets. It was always fun to watch the men work the nets. It was fun too, to watch the little fish slip out of the nets and swim away as though they were smiling at not getting caught.

The little fish! Koh's mouth dropped open. *Why I not thought of the little fish before? I catch and sell to fishermen!*

Koh knew it would take a long time to pick up a basket full of the little fish. But he knew the fishermen wanted to have all the fish possible at the end of the day. Koh decided, *I pick up every one I can! I sell cheap! Fishermen buy all right!*

Koh ran home and came back with a basket. He waded and picked up fish. He smiled when he got hold of them easily. His heart beat fast and his legs grew tired in the water when the fish slipped out of his hands. "I wade some more," he would say to himself. "Sometime I have basket full for sell fishermen!" So he worked along following the men who fished every day it wasn't storming.

When the fishermen stopped that evening, Koh's basket was full of fish. He offered to sell them, and the men quickly bought. They told him they would buy all he could pick up.

"Money for bamboo bank! Money for benches for house of living God!" Koh said over and over as he hurried toward home.

But the bank did not fill up very quickly. On stormy days when the men did not even try to fish, Koh would look out at the sea and say, "We never have this many rainy days in our village before!"

There were days when the little fish swam so quickly away that Koh could not catch enough to sell. Then he would think to himself, *Before I start catching, I happy to see little fish go free in the waters! Now I wish every little fish jump into Koh's basket!*

One day as the rain beat down on the roof of Koh's little bamboo hut he looked out the window and far down the winding road out of the village. *I try new way to earn money,* he thought. Even in the rain people and animals were on the road. Koh watched! *People! Animals!* he thought.

I know! Koh clapped his hands together with a plop. *People drive pigs on roads! Fishermen want pig-dung to feed fishes! I pick up feed for fishes, sell it to fishermen too!*

As Koh picked up, the basket didn't fill quickly at all. But Koh hunted and picked up. He hunted and picked up some more until his basket was full just as it was with the fishes sometimes.

The fishermen were glad to buy feed for the fish. They were always glad when Koh had a basket of little fish for them too. So all through the year Koh worked.

Sometimes on the way home with the few pennies in his hand, Koh would look at the sweets and the goodies to buy. "If I spend money, church of living God not get wood benches! Maybe with benches, more people come inside church and learn about true God!" he would tell himself.

Koh knew that the gods made of fish-skin and the other idols made of wood and stone that many people still prayed to could not take away sin. He knew that even when people prayed much and prayed loud and prayed long, that idols were hearing nothing and could not answer prayers. Koh knew that only the living Lord Jesus could take away drunkenness and quarreling, and stealing and other kinds of very bad sin. Koh wanted the church to be so nice that everybody in the village would want to come and hear about God.

One day Koh stood looking at his bamboo bank on the shelf. The time of the Chinese New Year's service was coming close. "Last year—New Year—we get bamboo banks!" Koh talked to himself as he lifted his bank. "It empty then. It heavier now!" the boy smiled.

Then the day of the New Year's service came. Many people sat on the dirt floor of the little church again. Most everyone was holding a little bamboo bank. Koh held his close up against him. He loved his little bamboo bank. "I not sad though, to have it break open. Then it will give money for benches. I get another bank to put more money in for something else for church of living God too." Koh said inside himself, watching other people with their banks.

Koh noticed baskets being passed for the money to be put into. Each person was breaking open his own bank and counting his money for God.

Then Koh gave a careful bend and twist to his bank. He didn't want the money to bounce out and roll away. With a little "crack" it popped open, and into Koh's lap fell $6.35.

The boy laid the money into the basket. A warm happy feeling floated around inside him. *Last year I wonder how I get money to help with benches. Funny, Koh, not remember very God who save from sin can help get money,* he thought.

And all the time I know well verse from God's book, "Blessed be the Lord, who daily loadeth us with benefits, even the God of our salvation" (Psalm 68:19).

Koh smiled as he looked around the little church. He thought, *soon we decide what we do for church of living God next year!*

6. AMAZING DISCOVERY FOR AZIM

Azim frowned as he stepped out of the thatch-roofed mission school set on a broad plain in India. Walking toward his own mud hut pressed close between two others, the boy wiggled his brown toes in the deep soft dust.

I'm very much tired of teacher and other boys all time wanting me be a Christian! I still go to gods in temple. I take rice and say prayer to those gods. I not wanting god I cannot at all see! he thought.

Azim reached down and picked up a handful of the powdery dust and threw it hard into the air.

The one road through the village was a winding road just wide enough for a bullock cart. Several clusters of the little mud houses with their courtyards, and the mission church and school made up the little village.

Azim turned from the road into an even more winding footpath, a space about four feet wide separating the courtyard walls.

The boy pushed open a door and stepped into his own courtyard. Two gray-black bullocks tethered near one wall were chewing sorghum fodder from wide clay pots.

Azim glanced at the three rope cots hanging from wooden pegs in one mud wall. *I glad when night come and we sleep in cots under bright stars,* he thought.

Father and Mother and Azim went to bed very early every night. There was not much oil for the little flat lamp. *I think hard tonight what I tell teacher and Christian boys tomorrow at school,* Azim thought looking again at the cots.

Darkness came in a few hours and the family climbed into their cots and slept.

Azim wakened several times. *The bullocks bad noisy tonight with their chewing!* he thought once. Another time, *They very much of the time moving a little tonight!*

Each time Azim was awake he thought of school tomorrow. I know! Azim's eyes opened wide in the darkness. *I just tell teacher and boys I accept the Jesus God, but I not really do it! I act like I take Him into my heart. I sing loud! I say prayers like Christians say! I just fool teacher and other boys!*

Azim dropped off to sleep. When he wakened Mother was cooking breakfast over the open fire in the courtyard.

Azim heard small children playing in the narrow pathway outside the door. Heavy footsteps meant that fathers were going down the pathways to the tiny farms to weed pigeon peas.

Azim jumped out of his cot. He ran to the corner of the courtyard near the bullocks and picked up his chopping knife. "Chop, chop, chop," went the knife in the boy's hands as he cut sorghum fodder into tiny pieces for the bullocks' morning meal.

For breakfast Mother baked some little flat cakes. She made them from meal that the day before she had ground between two heavy stones.

As the family ate, Azim put big pieces of white butter on his little flat cakes. Mother had churned the butter the morning before, then had clarified it by letting it simmer a long time over the open fire. Azim liked to watch Mother make butter!

But this morning Azim had a feeling inside him that he did not like much of anything. *But when I get to school, I going to act like I like everything and everybody,* he thought to himself. *That's the way Christian teacher and Christian boys act!*

In a little while Azim started down the footpath toward school. Before long he was back on the bullock road he had walked on the afternoon before.

As he walked, a bunch of pigeons fluttered over the boy's head, then landed on the ground ahead of him. A larger black bird lighted on the ground with them.

39

The pigeons ate quickly some grain that had dropped from an oxcart that had jiggled along the road. The black bird tried to eat, too, but the pigeons jumped at him. They pecked at the bird that was different. They made noises at him and he flew into the air.

Azim watched him as long as he could. But the bird was soon lost from sight as he flew toward the bright sunshine. "That bird know he not a pigeon!" Azim said half outloud. "Why he try eat with them? Pigeons not stand for that!"

Azim watched the pigeons for a long time. Suddenly a larger bird flew down among them again. It was a strange looking bird, black almost! But it had something white on its feathers. The black bird had found some ashes to put on himself.

The bird grabbed a few bites of food before the pigeons noticed the stranger among them. Then one pigeon spied him and jumped at him. Another pigeon saw him and pecked.

Other pigeons scratched him and bit into his feathers. "Squack! Screech! Scratch!" sounded among them as bird beat against bird. Feathers bounced into the air.

Silly black bird, Azim thought. *Did he think he could fool pigeons?*

The big bird, black now with the ashes gone off him, managed to get into the air again. Once more he flew into the sunlight and Azim was blinded as he looked. Thoughts began tumbling through Azim's mind.

The boy stood with his mouth open. His heart was pounding and he swallowed a big chunk of nothing.

I almost like that black bird myself! Azim stood motionless. *I on way to school to act like something I not!*

The boy looked down again at the pigeons. They were scratching in the dust, eating bits of something. Each one seemed happy and contented.

Pigeons have something black bird not have! Azim watched carefully. *But black bird smarter than Azim! Black bird want what he not have!*

40

Azim looked toward the school house. New thoughts came slipping into his mind. A warm happy feeling came over him as he stood there in the dusty road. *Right now I do what teacher and Christian boys long time want me do!* Azim raised his face toward heaven, his eyes squeezed tightly shut. He clasped his hands together under his chin and prayed, "Come into my heart, great God Lord Jesus. Forgive Azim's every sin! Make pure and clean for Jesus' sake, Amen!"

The boy ran as fast as he could to the school house. *Today I act exactly like Christian,* he thought. He knew the smile on his face was the biggest smile he had ever had. *Today Azim make big discovery by black bird! Today Azim act like Christian because he Christian!*

7.   A TIGER KILL A BULLOCK

"Oh sahib (Indian word for missionary or teacher), a tiger
kill a bullock!   Come quick!" Ram had reached his white
teacher Frank Wallin on the mission compound in India. "One
bullock stray while I herd.   I go to find.   Long time I hunt.
Then in leaves under trees at edge of jungle I find part-eaten
bullock.   I know tiger do it, sahib.   I prayed God help us kill
tiger!   You think God hear prayer, sahib?"

"Yes, Ram.   God always hears ours prayers.   He answers
the way He knows best.   Soometimes we have to help God do
the answering for He will not do for us what we can do for
ourselves."

The twelve-year-old boy looked at the teacher's anxious face.
The teacher said, "And a man-eater has just been reported on
this side of the pass!"

Ram's eyes opened wide, "Then we do very much to help
God answer prayer, huh sahib?   We pray God help!   We hunt
very hard!"

"Yes, Ram, we'll hunt very hard.   With the tiger on this
side of the pass, he must be killed," said missionary Wallin.

Frank Wallin, while a boy in Denmark had often read of
just such tiger terrors in India.   The boy often daydreamed of
some time being in that great land hunting fierce jungle
animals.

Then Frank and another boy who also wanted to see India
decided they must go to that land.   The boys did not have
money enough to buy costly tickets, but they each had a bicycle!

So over the countrysides of Europe the boys pedalled.   As
they rode they decided they would somehow go on around the
world.   Both boys were healthy and strong.   They had a little
money with them and they could earn more as they went. Yes,
they would go around the world!

But arriving in India, something happened to Frank Wallin. In that idol-blanketed land, the lad found the Lord Jesus as his Savior. In a little Danish mission station the adventure of a trip around the world faded away. The adventure of becoming a Christian missionary took its place.

Years of study and living among the people followed each other. Finally missionary Frank Wallin and his wife Thelma and their three little girls were stationed among Ram's people.

Now, with a man-eater to be found, Ram and two other boys were on their way back to the herd as sahib had instructed. To the south was the pass that Ram knew so well. The red rock floor down through it was smooth and flat and led out to great grassy plains below.

Many man-eaters known in grass plains! Ram thought as the boys ran. *But up over pass—*

The boys were soon with the herd of bullocks grazing near the jungle. In a few minutes, sahib and three other men arrived.

The two boys stayed with the herd. The men followed Ram and picked their way carefully toward the place of the dead bullock.

As they moved, everyone looked for signs of the tiger. They walked cautiously toward a lower piece of jungle jutting close to the pass with the red rock floor running through it.

"There, sahib! There under the leaves! See!" Ram pointed. Sahib went over to the animal.

"Perfect cover-job," sahib said. "And that water we passed right here close! Two things that almost prove the tiger will be back for another meal: his food all covered up, and drink close to it!" Sahib looked at the animal carefully. He said, "Neck broken, head neatly twisted around, haunches eaten, hidden under thorn and grass! A tiger might as well have left a sign saying he did it! And I'll venture he's not far away!"

Maybe he watching us, licking his tongue! Ram thought. The boy wiped dampness off his forehead.

The group picked their way back a little from the dead animal, and talked softly. They looked for a tree to hide in.

"The machan (rope platform) we bring, enough high in this tree?" one man asked.

"No!" another said frowning. "A tiger jump 16 feet up off ground! We have to have higher as that to be safe!"

"Here's good place, sahib!" Ram pointed to a tree with limbs just right to tie in the machan. "And high like no tiger can jump it!"

The machan was soon tied into the tree picked out, and plans made for the night's watch. One hunter and Ram would go back. Two hunters and sahib would go into the tree.

"No, sahib!" Ram's eyes begged. "I find dead buffalo. I stay and help find tiger!"

Sahib nodded. Two hunters returned to the compound.

The three climbed into the tree. Sahib had his gun, the hunter and Ram each with a spear.

Darkness came quickly. The slightest sound from the tree or the merest motion might scare away the killer that must be killed.

Sahib sat leaning against a limb, his rifle on his knees. The men were well hidden behind the branch-covering of their machan. But all had good leaf-chinked views out.

Mosquitos, ants, the scratch in the throat that called for a cough—none dared even be noticed. There *must* be no sound from the tree.

Somewhere a twig snapped below them. Ram's heart almost stopped beating. Two jackals called out that they had seen something. Ram felt his heart start to pound. He squeezed his eyes shut. *Ram can shut eyes without sound!* he thought. *I do better pray with eyes shut!* The boy listened again in the black silence. *We here in a tree, God! We try kill man-eating tiger! You listening, God? I pray like David, "Hear my prayer, O, Lord . . . in thy faithfulness answer me." You please help us kill tiger, God? Thank you, Amen!*

44

Ram opened his eyes and looked toward the dead bullock. The boy could feel that everyone in the tree was looking at exactly the same spot.

Then they all saw the killer. His face was ruffled and large. Sahib fired. The tiger rolled over, wounded. Sahib aimed again, and fired. But the hurt tiger lurched into the tall grass just in time not to catch the second shot.

"We stay up here now till daylight!" Ram cautioned.

"Yes, that old boy might still have plenty of pounce in him," sahib answered. The three watched and waited for the first streaks of dawn.

With the very first light, they crawled out of the tree and began hunting the tiger. They came to the jungle fireline (a wide clearing cut through the jungle as a firebreak), and on the other side lay the pain-maddened beast.

Sahib fired! The animal jumped, just missing the shot. He sprang several feet into the air landing just before reaching the three.

He wheeled around and went back to his exact spot over the fireline! As he moved the three dashed into the nearest trees.

From his tree Ram watched sahib's every move. *He can't get good aim! His tree no good tree to try to kill tiger from!* Ram peered through the leaf-covered branches.

Just then sahib dropped and changed trees. He was only up a few feet when the tiger reached the ground right under him.

Ram gave a limb above him a jerk so he could see better. "Tiger get sahib!" Ram screamed inside him. "He get sahib sure!"

Then he saw sahib's head bump a limb and saw his topi (cork helmet) hit the ground. The tiger pounced onto the topi. Even in pain, the tiger played with the new jungle toy.

While he played, sahib quickly climbed higher and higher. As he climbed, the beast, teeth buried in the topi walked back to his spot over the fireline. There he sat down.

Sahib shot once. The tiger crumpled, dead. He lay ready to be measured and skinned.

The three came out of the lower jungle and moved up the slope. Down the slope the native pastor and another native were hurrying to meet them. The pastor said, "After you left yesterday we felt there was something wrong. So we asked the people to gather and pray. We started out then this morning to see if we could find you."

Sahib quickly told of the tiger's finish, giving every detail of the topi plaything.

Ram's eyes opened wider and wider as he listened to sahib. "God not only guide David's stone when he throw at great Goliath, He guide topi right into tiger's mouth here in jungle, huh sahib?" Ram felt a happiness cover the whole inside of him. He thought, *I wondered if God hear prayer of Ram to help kill very bad tiger! With my own eyes I see great God answer prayer!*

8. I AM NOW AMOS

Dhan (Dawn) sat on the ground under a low palm tree in India, chewing on a piece of hard white coconut. *I do love Lord Jesus the new sahib tells about,* the boy thought to himself. *But my brother, Manohar, he very not at all understand. He goes all the time to temple to pray there to cow!*

Back of Dhan, little gray monkeys ran up and down the tree trunk. They jumped from the tree to the boy's shoulders. They ran from his shoulders to his feet and wiggled his brown toes in their leathery little hands.

Dhan did some more thinking, *I know cow in temple still only cow! Even gold paint on horn and many flowers on string around neck, still only cow. Still cannot love Dhan and Manohar and Father and Mother like good God in heaven love everybody!*

Dhan pushed himself to his feet and threw his last bite of coconut on the ground for the monkeys.

The boy moved slowly toward his own hut. Night soon came and Mother had white fluffy rice for the family to eat.

The meal finished, Father, Mother, Manohar and Dhan unrolled their pallets on the floor for the night's sleeping. It was black outside now. Dhan lay down on his pallet. He closed his eyes, but not in sleep. The boy was thinking and thinking.

One part of Dhan's heart was singing for joy because he had accepted the Lord Jesus as his very own Savior. One part was sad! Very sad! *I give anything if only Manohar love heavenly God, too, just anything!* Dhan thought in the stillness. *Then whole family would be Christian. But when Father and Mother and I talk about living God, Manohar stick fingers in ears! Sometimes he even make faces!* Dhan blinked in the blackness. *He two years younger, usually copy all I do! I just keep on pray for him that he soon love Lord Jesus!*

Dhan lay thinking how good the living God had been to him all of his thirteen years. He had heard Father and Mother tell how sometimes the earth did not give rice enough for all the people to eat. Then there was sadness. There was great trouble. Sometimes the people would all have to leave their villages and go far, far away hunting food. But so long as Dhan could remember, his village had always had rice enough to eat.

Dhan remembered Father and Mother describing the houses they had to live in when they had to leave their own village. Sometimes then they had no real houses at all. But here at home Dhan liked his comfortable house.

This house was made of mud, whitewashed on the outside with bright colored dots on the whitewash here and there to scare off the evil spirits. The house was painted before any of the family became Christians, and Manohar had begged them to leave the painting as it was.

In the front of Dhan's house was a low door and one window. The room at the front of the house was a dark little room where the cow stayed at night. In the daytime, Father drove the cow through the village, down past the back doors of the houses so he could sell milk. Cooks who wanted to buy milk would come to the back door with a little tin pail and Father would milk right into the pail. The cooks would pay him, and he would go on to another house.

Early next morning before the sun was even up, Dhan heard a high-pitched bird cry screetch through the air. The crow on the top of the clothesline pole was doing her every-morning waking up! As she screeched, dozens of other birds started their morning noises too. Then other dozens of birds sang and chirped until a regular bird concert was going. Every morning when the weather was warm and dry this very bird music was heard.

In each June and each November though, great winds called the monsoons would come blowing in from the ocean, bringing rain. Then the rivers would become raging torrents and the dry parched land would become soaked.

Now it was between monsoon seasons and the weather was warm and comfortable for everyone to go barefoot. The men and boys wore no clothes at all except *dhotis,* cotton cloth wound around their hips and between their legs making something like knee pants for them.

Dhan stood to his feet, and loosely put on his dhoti. He ran into the garden and stepped up a piece of old tree stump which served as the bathing place. The religion the family grew up with made it a law that no one enter the kitchen in the mornings without first washing from head to foot. Now that they were Christians, all but Manohar, they knew they should be clean so they kept on following the custom.

Dhan washed quickly, not because his heart told him he had to please a god, but he liked the feeling of being fresh and clean for the living God.

A little copper bell tinkled from the kitchen. *"Chapati* are ready!" Dhan said to himself, and hurried into the house.

Dhan liked *chapati,* the small wheat pancakes with *ghee,* a sort of butter served with them. Coconuts right off the coconut tree in the yard furnished milk for everyone a good breakfast drink.

Dhan liked it that they could bow their heads and say thank you to God for their food just as they did in the mission school. He looked up from the prayer and Manohar was already eating. Dhan said another quick prayer for his brother, then looked across at Mother. She looked so pretty with four rings in her ears, and a bright little jewel on the left side of her nose. The two dots of orange-colored powder she put on her forehead every morning were a sign of the caste to which she belonged.

Dhan looked at the dots and thought, *Is good sahib is teaching that in sight of God, is no caste at all. Some day Mother not wear dots on forehead!*

Weeks and months slipped by, and Dhan kept on studying

49

hard in the mission school. Manohar kept on going to the temple to pray to the flower decked cow. Dhan's love for God became greater and greater as time went by.

Then one day Dhan did not feel well and was examined by the Christian mission doctor. The doctor made many tests and gave Dhan medicine to take. "When the reports from the tests are ready I shall bring them to your home," the doctor told Dhan's family.

One warm afternoon Father and Mother and Manohar and Dhan all sat in the open courtyard with the mission doctor. He held in his hands many papers.

The doctor spoke in a low kind voice. "Dhan," he said.

Dhan felt a strange uneasiness come over him just the tender way the doctor spoke his name. Dhan dampened his dry lips with his tongue.

The doctor continued, "The examinations show that you have Hansen's disease, leprosy, Dhan."

Dhan's mouth dropped open. Something inside him screamed. "No! It can't be! It can't be leprosy!" Then Dahn looked straight into the eyes of Manohar. Dhan remembered the words he had often said, *"I give anything to have Manohar know great God, Lord Jesus as Savior too!"* His heart pounded wildly as thoughts tumbled over each other. *Maybe I give everything! I give up home, I go live in leper colony now! I give up school! I give up friends! If this win Manohar to Lord Jesus, I give gladly!*

Dhan felt his head nodding up and down. The doctor had an amazed look on his face when Dhan could again see clearly. There were tears in Mother's eyes. Father was swallowing, chewing his lips, squeezing his fingers in his tightly folded-together hands. Manohar sat looking down, just looking down!

A few days later Dhan walked slowly into the Christian leprosarium. Here day by day, month by month, the loving kindness of the Lord Jesus was extended to him in the medical care. Here he found he could still study. For a school just

50

as thé one in his village, gave the lepers a chance to learn, too.

And best of all, here, Dhan continued to grow in the Lord. *"I want to do something for my wonderful Savior!"* Dhan said to himself over and over. *"I want some day for Manohar to be Christian. I want to tell many people about great living God!"*

One day Dhan felt warm and happy inside as he sat listening to the pastor in the leprosarium telling a Bible story. The pastor said, "Hundreds of years before the Lord Jesus came into the world there was a farmer boy whose name was Amos."

I like that name Amos, Dhan thought.

"Day after day the boy watched his father's sheep, plowed the fields and picked the fruit from the orchard," the pastor continued.

I like that boy Amos, too, Dhan thought again.

The pastor said, "The boy Amos did very great thinking while he was doing his work. And he did not swear when the bullocks refused to pull the plow. He did not goad them with a sharp pointed stick until the blood ran down their backs when they were stubborn. Amos sang as he followed the plow. Most of his songs came from the Psalms of David. Amos loved the God of Abraham, of Joseph, of Daniel and Elijah."

That Amos, I like better and better! Dhan thought.

The pastor said again, "One day God told Amos that he wanted him to give up his plowing. He wanted him to begin preaching!"

Begin preaching! Dahn thought the words almost out loud.

"And though Amos had never been to Bible school," the pastor looked straight at Dhan it seemed to him, "Amos listened to the word of God. He had a vision, too, from God to prophesy and he did just what God told him to do. In the book that Amos later wrote, forty times or more he said, 'Thus saith the Lord,' or words meaning that very thing!"

Thus saith the Lord! Dhan thought to himself. *He is saying to me to preach His word. I do not know how it shall be, but*

51

I start right now to plan to preach it. I even now take to myself the name Amos!"

One wonderful happy day not too much later, the doctor pronounced the leprosy dormant in the young man now Amos. The doctor gave Amos a clean bill of health, so once again he could go to his family and friends.

Before he left the leprosarium, the Christian lepers decided they would pay all of his Bible school training expenses.

"Out of your fifteen cents a month each, you pay for my schooling?" Amos asked as tears filled his eyes.

"Yes, we too want to preach, and we preach through you," the Christian friends said.

So Amos left the leprosarium to begin his schooling to preach. He walked first toward his own village to tell his family and friends of his wonderful decision and of the lepers' help to him. As he walked, he rejoiced in God with each step. Though his face had the marks of the disease he had suffered, and though he had only stubs for fingers and toes, he went singing.

At home, Amos quietly opened the courtyard door. Mother ran to him from her grain-grinding stones. Father dashed from the plow blade he was fastening on to a long handle. Manohar dropped his chopping knife where he was cutting fodder for the bullocks.

"Our Dhan!" Mother cried.

"Another man in the family," Father said proudly.

"My brother!" shouted Manohar.

The preaching one explained his new name to his family. They had visited with him only a few times while he was gone so now there was much talking of all the things each had to tell.

The new Amos looked around the courtyard. He looked toward the kitchen and the other rooms he loved so well.

"How good to be home! O, how good! O, how good! But

52

I go again on the morrow to start in the Bible school. I want to learn to tell many people about the great Lord Jesus!"

Manohar walked to the side of his brother. He said tenderly, "You talked to me about Lord Jesus before you got very bad sickness. I not listen then. I think—" Manohar put his head down. "I guess I think then you soon give up notion about new God!" Manohar looked up at his taller brother. "But when you are so long time sick, and you come home still happy in your great God—" Manohar paused.

Amos began breathing faster. *Can it be?* he thought. Prayer flowed all around in Dhan's mind. *O Lord God, may it be so! May it be so!*

Manohar's voice sounded in Amos' ears again, "I too take today this same Lord Jesus as my Savior."

Amos dropped to his knees, joy filling his soul. Father, Mother and Manohar all knelt in prayer. Amos heard his own voice saying over and over, "Thank you God! Thank you great, wonderful Lord Jesus! Thank you for giving to Manohar love for living God in heaven!"

9. LEOPARD HUNT FOR SUNTOSH

Suntosh (Sun' tosh) watched every move of his buffalo as he herded them close to the edge of the missionary compound.

"I wanted go hunt leopard, too! Those mean fierce animals! They worser even than tigers! But no! This time men say, 'You boy, you herd buffalo.' " Suntosh eyed the buffalo carefully.

A leopard had slipped into the native village the night before and had carried away a dog. Suntosh knew the dread of the leopard to every person and every village in the jungles of India.

For a leopard could jump through the window of a hut and carry away a person. He could jump up onto the grass roofs and tear a hole for an entrance.

Suntosh watched in every direction. He knew that people in some of the villages became so frightened when a leopard made a kill among them that the whole village life was changed. No one would go to the fields to work. No one would herd buffalo. Everyone stayed inside the huts and kept very still, very, very still!

"Crack!" went a gun shot. A man's scream followed. The sounds came from the tangled trees close on the right of the buffalo.

Suntosh looked at the great beasts, then toward the trees where the sound had come from. Another scream!

"I must go to man!" Suntosh said to the buffalo! "May true God in heaven herd buffalo for Suntosh!" he prayed.

Suntosh ran toward the sounds, holding his spear high. He saw people running from the village, too. Suntosh was led to the man by loud groanings.

The man tried to talk. "The hunters go early—I not in village then—when I get back I go to catch up. I see leopard! I shoot." The man grew silent.

54

Suntosh felt shaky inside. "What I do?" he said almost screaming. The other people had not arrived.

The man spoke again. "He act like he have broken back. He drag away when I scream."

Missionary Howard Johnson and the natives from the village reached the man.

The man said no more. Suntosh spoke as the missionary examined the wounded man. "He say he shoot leopard, but not kill him! Leopard have broken back, he think!"

"We'll get the man to the hospital. It's thirty miles, so we'll have to hurry. When we get back we'll go after the leopard." The missionary spoke quickly.

Suntosh felt his heart thump against his chest. He knew how frightened the others were now that a person had been attacked by a leopard. The hunters might not be back for a long, long, time. *Someone must go with the missionary when he go after leopard!* Suntosh thought.

The missionary spoke, "Suntosh, you were with the man while he was still speaking. You come with me to the hospital. Dinker and Lalys, you bring in the buffalo. With the leopard still loose, the animals better be in their pens."

The hurt man was carried back to the village and gently laid into the truck. The road to the hospital was good all the way; so they were there in a little while.

The man stayed at the hospital. Riding back to the village, Suntosh said to the missionary, "I go with you to hospital! I go with you when you go after leopard, sahib? Suntosh watched sahib Johnson.

"Do you think you're brave enough, Suntosh? You know how fierce leopards are! The missionary looked down the road as he talked.

"I brave, sahib. Anyway this leopard may have broken back!"

The missionary smiled. Then he looked as he did sometimes in the boy's classroom in lesson time. He said, "One with a

55

spear and one with a gun, and both trusting in God, we'll trust we get the leopard, Suntosh."

"I go then, sahib! I go with you! I go with you!"

Suntosh looked at the missionary. "Thank you, sahib. O, thank you!"

The two hurried over the miles and turned in on the compound and parked the truck. The missionary with his gun and Suntosh with his spear were soon carefully picking their way where the man had been mauled by the leopard.

They talked softly. "If leopard have broken back, he not climb tree. That one good thing." Suntosh was close to the sahib. The two followed the trail of blood, stepping without a sound.

Jungle animals around them seemed to sense a killer some where among them. A few yards away deer were calling. Just beyond the swampy ground they were getting into, a herd of cheetal were barking.

Then they heard him. The beast crashed some bushes behind them.

Sahib swung around, taking his aim. He fired. Only a click! The bullet was a dud!

Before he could reload and shoot, the spotted cat was upon him. Suntosh's spear was knocked from his hand. The spear was under the leopard and the sahib.

A claw gashed open a wound in sahib's forehead. Another sank deep into an arm.

For a second the leopard's head was between sahib's legs. Suntosh saw the legs squeeze. "Choke him, sahib! Choke him!" he screamed. "You leopard! You not have very bad broken back!" Suntosh screamed at the leopard.

Suntosh watched for a chance to grab his spear. He prayed, "Please, good Lord God, kill mean, bad leopard. Help sahib, please, help sahib!"

The leopard jerked loose. The missionary jumped to his feet. The leopard stood exactly over the spear. Sahib flipped the dud from the gun, slipped in another bullet and fired.

Another weak crack! Once more a dud!

Suntosh watched the animal. "It very bad hurt animal, all right! It not move quick like. It getting ready do something though!" Suntosh wanted to scream. He wanted to grab his spear and pierce the animal. He wanted to do—anything—to help the sahib!

But he stood motionless and prayed. "Please make leopard not jump again." He watched the sahib's quick move as he jerked out the dud and slipped in one more bullet.

Sahib was praying too. Suntosh heard words, "Please God, please help us now!"

A loud shot almost knocked Suntosh over. Sahib had fired. The big spotted leopard rolled over dead.

The villagers heard the shot. Within minutes they were with sahib and Suntosh. They bandaged sahib's gashed forehead and put a tourniquet on his ripped arm.

Soon sahib was carefully helped into the truck. Suntosh crawled in beside him. Someone drove them again to the hospital.

"Sahib, you remember that verse you teach boys in Bible class, '...God hath power to help...' (II Chronicles 25:8)? Today Suntosh see that great power!"

10. LONG TIME I THINK

On a hot afternoon in India, Akanya (A kan´ ya) sat with sixteen other boys on the hard dirt floor of the mission school.

Some of the boys wiggled, and little noises sounded in the room. But Akanya sat straight and still. He listened to every word the teacher said.

The teacher was telling how sin had come into the world when Adam and Eve, the very first people disobeyed. "But God planned a way for Adam and Eve and for all the people who would ever be born into the world to have their sins forgiven," the teacher said. "People could trust in God and bring sacrifices to His name. God would look upon the hearts longing to be forgiven and would cleanse them from every wrong."

Akanya wiggled a little now. *He's coming to part of story I do not yet believe!* Akanya thought.

The teacher's next words were, "Then one day God sent His own Son, the Lord Jesus into the world to be the sacrifice for all people who would accept Him into their hearts."

Akanya felt his forehead wrinkle as one thought after another came to him. *I not think God could give up own Son to be sacrifice!*

The teacher's words continued, "To be a sacrifice, Jesus must die. He knew that He came into the world for that reason. While He was on earth He said, 'For this is my blood of the new testament, which is shed for many for the remission of sins' (Matthew 26:28)."

Akanya bit the inside of his right cheek, *Long time I think before I believe one give up own son to die!*

Akanya was so busy thinking he didn't even hear the teacher's next words. The boys around him began moving. Then

Akanya heard the teacher say school was dismissed for the day.

On the way home, the dark skinned boy kicked clouds of dust into the air with each step. *I not say one thing to Father and Mother about what I not believe in mission school. Many Hindu boys not get to go school at all! And I love mission school!*

A school was unusual in the kind of village that Akanya lived in. For his was a village where the people made mud houses and clay dishes. The people were all very poor. But one day a man who called himself Teacher John had come to the village and said he would teach the boys. He said the fathers would have to make a little mud school house first, though.

The boys all coaxed the fathers to let them have a school. So a little hut was built and Teacher John came to the village to live and to teach.

Teacher John had showed the villagers how to keep the streets clean. He showed the people how to white-wash their houses. He taught the boys how to read out of books and sing songs he called hymns. And Teacher John, each day in school, taught of a living God who loves everybody.

That living God loves even the poor people like we are! Akanya thought as he neared his own white-washed hut.

In his home, Akanya greeted Mother, then went quickly to the family's tiny field. There he drove the oxen around and around and around the well of water. Buckets were fastened on a rope dropped into the well, and the rope was fastened to the oxen. With the oxen moving, moving, moving, the buckets were drawn up and the water emptied into a ditch to flow out to the grain field.

As Akanya walked and walked driving the oxen, he thought again of the teacher's words about God giving His Son to die. *Would my father give me to die? No!* Akanya tapped an oxen that slowed up a bit.

The oxen kept moving in endless circles. Water kept empty-

59

ing into the ditch. Thoughts kept chasing each other around in Akanya's mind. And then the sky colors began rapidly changing. Night was beginning to come.

Without knowing how they started, movement and noises were all around Akanya. The roads were crowded with men and boys going home from their fields. Cartmen were singing, each trying to be louder than the others, it seemed. *That's way cartmen scare off evil spirits!* Akanya thought to himself. *Big noises keeps lonseome away too!*

Then, just at dark, as Akanya reached home, the drums began beating. "Tom-tom-te-tom-tom," came the rhythm of a familiar song. This lasted a short time, then suddenly, "Boom!" went the temple drums. They were silent a while, then began again softly.

Akanya's family sat on the floor and ate their evening meal of rice and curry. The lights were soon put out and the family lay on their mats to sleep. Oil must be used sparingly, in poor villages.

Akanya lay very still and listened as the jackals began to cry. Dogs howled a sad answer. Drums in the nighttime began beating louder and louder.

Trees moving in the wind made swishy noises. Small night-prowling animals began running and squeaking. The drums in the temple kept up their "Boom! Boom! Boom!"

Akanya wished he could sleep. But faster and faster, louder and louder went the temple drums. *Are the drums saying No! No! One does not give of own to die!* he wondered.

Akanya's eyes blinked in the night's blackness. In his ears the drums seemed to be beating, *Don't you believe what you hear in mission school about God giving own Son to die!*

Then, "Crash!" sounded the cymbals in the last note from the drums. Only the whine of mosquitoes continued as Akanya dropped off to sleep.

The next sound Akanya heard was that of Mother moving

60

around in the room. That meant it was morning, but Akanya and Father did not move on their mats.

Hindu mothers arise first. They get up mornings while the stars are yet in the sky. First of all the mothers make themselves clean and neat. Then they say their prayers, sitting with the house very silent. Day comes closer and closer.

Akanya acted as if he were sleeping as he watched Mother move from her prayers and begin preparing food for the family.

Food preparation for the Hindus is almost sacred. The mother first puts on a fresh, clean dress. The dress is beautiful enough to worship in. All day long after she begins cooking, the mother does not touch any person, and no other person is allowed in the place where the cooking is being done.

Akanya peeked at Mother through brown fingers held over his eyes. The food was almost ready. Father wiggled. The boy thought, *Could one of us give up other for die?*

Then Father moved to the edge of his mat. Akanya sat up, stretched both arms into the air, then stood to his feet and dashed out the door. Father followed him slowly and the two washed at the family washing place outside under the sky.

Father and Akanya washed their own clothes as they bathed, for that was the way the families in Akanya's village all did.

Then around the sacred *tulsi* plant growing on a pedestal in the front of the house, Father walked saying many prayers. Father fingered his rosary as he walked, and chanted verses from the Hindu's most holy scriptures.

Akanya tried to keep his mind on the Hindu scriptures as he did his chanting. But it seemed that the living God in heaven was near and was saying, "You need not chant and rub your rosary, Akanya."

Akanya turned and looked in every direction. Father glanced at him and Akanya quickly began chanting again.

Soon after the praying, Mother served breakfast of tea and bread. Then school hours followed with more lessons and more Bible study.

61

At 2:30 when school was just ready to start after the long noon rest, small children's happy shouting was heard by the school boys. Up the street came a big elephant with the little prince and princess of the province riding high on the elephant's back.

Little prince, Akanya thought, *one day be king of whole province. He already dressed rich like king! Pink turban high above head; tall gold feather in front pointing to sky!*

Akanya stood breathless, watching. *Gold chains! Gold rings!* He thought to himself, *Could his father give him for die? Never!*

The little prince and princess rode on toward another village and the boys went in to their lessons. As they went inside, Akanya thought, *It's fun having little boy prince in province!*

Akanya had heard that in the province next to theirs a new little baby prince had recently been born. Akanya smiled to himself as he thought, *I wonder when he ride through province on elephant!*

When school was out that afternoon Akanya hurried home to ask Mother and Father if they too had seen the royal visitors. Akanya talked first with Mother in the little white-washed hut. Even with the hut close to the road Mother had not seen the prince and princess ride into the village. "Maybe at well getting water," Mother said sadly.

Just then, "Boom!" went the sound of the village drum that meant for villagers to gather quickly at the chieftain's hut.

"What, my Mother?" Akanya asked, his throat getting tight.

"We must fast run, Akanya!" Mother answered.

Villagers soon stood before the chieftain. Beside him stood a runner from the next province, Chitor. The chieftain quickly told the villagers the message the runner had brought. The wicked Mogul, Humayun, and his warriors who had conquered so much of northern India had pushed into Chitor. They were trying to kill the royal family so Humayun could be the ruler of Chitor.

Chitor! thought Akanya. *That where new baby prince is!*

The chieftain said sadly, "Queen Mother there already killed! But baby prince Udai Singh, rescued by friends. He taken to a mother Purmea, already with baby same age. They hope to fool enemies when come, thinking no royal family there!"

The tall chieftain listened to more the runner had to say, then told more to the villagers. "Enemies go away from Chitor for while. Then in night come to home of Purmea. Purmea know why warriors come! They come to kill baby prince! Purmea quick put sleeping prince in fruit basket. She cover basket with cloth and give maid to take far away for safe hiding. Then Purmea put kiss on forehead of own sleeping baby and throw royal blanket on him!"

Akanya's mouth dropped open. The boy snatched a look toward the school house. *To die!* screamed in his mind. *That mother give own baby die for baby prince!*

There in the crowd of villagers huddled before the chieftain and runner, Akanya lifted his eyes toward the heavens.

The boy prayed silently, *Great living God who love everybody! Long time I think about God giving own Son to die! Now my heart say "True it is He die on cross for sins of whole world, for Akanya!"*

I now believe! I now take for very own Savior!

11. MADDHU AND THE TIGER

Maddhu sat on the dirt floor of the little mission schoolhouse high in the hills of India. He listened as the white teacher told again of the wonderful Lord Jesus.

Maddhu loved the Lord Jesus and loved the white teacher who had come to tell about Him. *I want to do something good for sahib! I want to do something to show that I love him,* he thought to himself. His heart beat fast as he sat thinking.

When class was over, the boys trotted off to the work each had to do. Maddhu started down the hill to herd buffalo. Up the hill through the tangle of trees came loud voices. Excited voices!

Maddhu dashed down the hill. He was glad he was twelve. Some of the fastest runners on the whole mission compound were twelve—and some of the very best hunters!

Then Maddhu saw people. They were coming up the hill carrying something—or somebody!

Maddhu reached the group, and he saw a limp figure. He saw blood and torn clothing, and a great open wound on an arm.

Ohhhhh, the hurt one is our evangelist! Maddhu thought.

The boy turned and ran toward the mission bungalow. "Sahib Olson! Sahib Olson! The evangelist is hurt! A tiger, a tiger!"

Sigurd Olson, the missionary in charge of the Christian work in the great hill section of western India, stepped to the bungalow veranda.

"They're coming, sahib! Carrying the evangelist! A tiger—" Maddhu felt almost as if he had seen the tiger strike. He had always known tiger fierceness! He had lived all his life in the jungle.

Maddhu pointed down the hill as the carriers came into sight.

Sahib and he dashed into the bungalow and pulled a table into the middle of one of the rooms. The carriers arrived with the evangelist, and sahib worked quickly and quietly with him. Sahib bent his head low every little while to hear what the hurt man was saying.

When the man was bandaged and laid on clean white sheets on the bed, sahib stepped out to the veranda again. Maddhu stayed close by. It was he who had come with the news to sahib!

Sahib looked at the crowd of excited natives. He looked at Maddhu and said quietly, "There's a wounded tiger in the jungle. The evangelist shot him but didn't kill him. He's afraid it will attack someone else as it did him."

Maddhu's eyes blinked fast. "That tiger will be worse fiercer now, sahib! A tiger in pain, Ohhhh, he's a bad one!"

"I know, Maddhu. I'm going to take my gun and go to the jungle and see if I can get him. The men are too excited and afraid to do any good going with me."

Maddhu spoke quickly, "I go with you. More boys from the school and I go with you, find tiger! We must kill tiger, sahib!"

Sahib went after his gun. Maddhu got a dozen boys, each armed with an ax or a spear, and soon they all edged into the jungle.

A little ahead and to one side someone spotted grass swaying slowly, slowly. Sahib and the boys stood still. The grass moved again. A sambar (a large brown Asiatic deer) raised its head from the spot and bellowed an alarm.

"He smells us—or maybe the tiger," Maddhu spoke softly. "Maybe the fierce one is near!"

Sahib and the boys sneaked to the spot. The sambar moved away—moved without a sound. Sahib whispered, "Maybe the tiger went up along the ridge. There's no blood to follow. We'll just trust God to lead us!"

All eyes strained for signs. Ears listened for every sound.

The group edged out of the grass and picked their way through a tangle of shrubs and trees.

A monkey sat on the drooped end of a tree branch. He was motionless, watching something below him.

Maddhu bent forward and looked beyond the shrubs. "I think—" Maddhu dampened his lips with his tongue, then whispered, "I think tiger right there below monkey!"

Sahib stepped forward, his gun in his hand. A great streak raised from the shrubs and shot through the air. The man had no time to fire. One hand gripped the butt of the gun, the other slid to the end of the barrel. The tiger's teeth clamped down on the barrel just missing both hands.

Man and beast hit the ground with a thud. Maddhu's spear struck quickly into the fierce one. Other spear and ax blows struck. Monkeys screamed from every direction. The big brown sambar stood motionless on a ridge above the tall grasses.

The tiger lay dead and ugly. The boys pulled sahib to his feet. Maddhu's heart was beating hard as it had when he had sat in the schoolroom. Inside him was a prayer, *Thank you great God in heaven for letting me help kill tiger! For letting me do something good for sahib!*

To sahib Maddhu said, "God answer prayer and lead us to tiger! Then like good Book say, 'The Lord God is my strength...' (Habakkuk 3:19), He help us kill tiger too!"

12. RAMJI'S VERY FIRST CHRISTMAS

Ramji (Ram ji) thin and dark skinned, walked slowly along the slick muddy path toward his own village in India. With every step, he thought harder and harder. He had been visiting a neighboring village where every week an Indian lady came to tell Jesus-stories.

As Ramji walked he talked to himself, "This Jesus One, He very fine God! I know He fine God, I take Him into my heart and now all the time would like be happy. No more do bad sins make me inside all grumpy! But Father and Mother—" The soft mud oozed up between Ramji's toes as he stepped. "Father and Mother still worship monkey god, so sometimes heart is sad thinking about them."

The boy looked far ahead to the little mud huts of his own village. He was glad it was still a long way off. He would have time to do praying as he walked. He would think hard how to help Father and Mother believe.

Ramji had been in the same neighboring village the first day the lady had come there to tell Jesus-stories. She had looked kind and had smiled right at Ramji! It was summer then, and hot! Very hot!

She had said, "Can we find a nice shady place under a tree where we can sit down and talk?"

Ramji had stood still like a tree trunk. *Say more! Please say more!* he had thought quickly. The lady's voice was like beautiful music. Her face was happy looking, like nothing Ramji had ever seen before.

"Can anyone in this village read?" The lady smiled at the boys and girls and at the fathers and mothers who were gathering around her. Ramji moved in closer.

Read? Any of us read? Ramj thought to himself. He could

feel hot breath coming out of his wide open mouth. He had wished for so long that he could read! *Does she want us to read to her? She can't read to us! She's a woman, and women can't read! What she mean?* Words tumbled around in Ramji's mind.

Ramji watched the lady's every move. *Can she be only spirit, maybe able to do magic?* he thought.   He moved closer and his hand touched her sari. He jumped. *She real!* he thought, almost saying it out loud.

Then a village man spoke. "We cannot read! We never have school in this village. In other village, that way—" the man pointed over his right shoulder, "some can read! Some even can write!"

Then the lady asked, "Would you like to have a school?"

A school in this village! Ramji thought to himself. *Sometimes then I maybe come too! Some day then I know what paper say only to people who read!*

"If you will build the schoolhouse, I will come and help boys and girls learn to read," the lady said.

"But girls cannot learn to read!" a man said, and all the men laughed and laughed.

"Do you really mean *you* help them learn read?" another man spoke more kindly. "You surely not read, huh?"

The lady said, "Does anyone here have a book?"

"I have!" a man said quickly.   "And I know what book say! A boy from a school village get it from teacher.   I sit with boy long time and he tell me over and over until I can say what book say. Haaaa! Let lady try read my book!"

The man ran to his hut and returned with the book. The kind look was still on the lady's face. She took the book gently in her smooth looking hands, and opened the book to the first pages. She spoke slowly from it, "Boys and girls, we are going to run a race today."

The man stared at the lady.

The lady read again, "One of us will carry a load on his back. Will he be able to run as fast as the others?"

The man was not laughing now. He only stood looking. Looking right at the lady!

Then the man had a big happy smile. "She reads! She reads good my book! Girls can learn to read. My own little girl, she can learn read!"

Then all at once there was big talking and all kinds of good happiness. Fathers began saying just where the schoolhouse should be built. Everyone smiled at the new lady.

Ramji edged close to the lady and asked if he might come sometimes and learn to read too. She said he could come, and that they would not wait until the schoolhouse was built but would start school under the trees.

The lady began teaching that very day. Then she came to the village week after week and taught boys and girls and sometimes men and women too.

The men found a high place in the village where it would not be too muddy when the rains came, and they started work. The women helped too, carrying baskets of clay to make strong walls. Trees were cut to frame the roof, and great bunches of straw were piled on and tied tight to the frame. The men let Ramji help tie on straw. He felt so good, he was helping build the schoolhouse!

When the school was finished the pupils sat in a circle on the dirt floor. White sand from the river's edge was put inside the circle, and each pupil made letters in the sand with a finger.

Ramji came to the school every day that he did not have to help his father work. He learned to read. He learned to write. But best of all the smiling lady taught the boys and girls about the Lord Jesus coming into the world to save people from their sins.

Ramji tried sometimes to tell Father and Mother about the Lord Jesus. But Father did not like to hear and did not like

69

Mother to listen either. So Ramji knew he would have to quit going to school if Father became too displeased.

So, today as Ramji walked home along the muddy path he thought of Father and Mother still worshipping the monkey god. Ramji's whole heart would be so happy if they only knew his God, the Lord Jesus! *Help me Lord God, great God, good God!* he prayed as he walked. *Help me show them your way!*

Ramji began singing the words they had been practicing at school for the Christmas program. "Jesus the Savior is born!" He had sung his songs many times, softly so Father would not be cross, yet loud enough for him to hear. *Maybe I sing things what I dare not say,* he thought. Ramji could hardly wait for the program!

For the program, the teacher and all the school and many fathers and mothers were going to the big village where there was a real church. People from villages all over the hills were invited.

In the church they would sing songs. They would say verses from the Bible about God up in heaven and how He sent His Son the Lord Jesus to be Savior. Ramji was invited to ride along with the school in one of the ox carts.

Ramji arrived at his clean one room home and went inside. Father and Mother and all six of Ramji's little brothers and sisters were ready to eat their evening rice and curry.

Ramji's heart pounded against his chest as words tumbled from his lips about the Christmas program and his invitation to go.

"I go, Father, please, I go?" Ramji pleaded, his mouth dry and hot.

A different look than Father usually had crossed his face. He said slowly, "You go, son! You go! Say no more! But you go!"

Ramji looked from Father to Mother. Father began eating

70

rice quickly. Mother looked down into her bowl made of baked clay.

Ramji trembled inside. *He said I go! He not even bad cross this time!* he thought. "Thank you, Father," he finally managed to say.

The day of the program, Ramji rode with the boys and girls and teachers from the school. Arriving at the big village they saw little bonfires burning all over the hillsides as family groups were cooking their rice. Nine hundred men and women and boys and girls had come from the villages into the mission compound. Ramji's school joined other schools and they went singing from group to group on the hillsides.

Then into the church they went, and they sang and they sang of the Lord Jesus.

On the platform for the program, Ramji looked over the many, many faces. Here and there was one that looked cross as Father did sometimes. But as the singing went on and the Bible verses were said, not a face that Ramji saw looked cross anymore.

Then after preaching the message of Jesus' birthday, the preaching man said to the people, "Will boys and girls please come to platform again? We all bow heads and very soft sing Silent Night! Maybe somebody tonight wants birthday too! new life from this night on—in great God, Lord Jesus!" The preaching man waited, he looked at the great crowd of people.

Then he said again, "If anyone takes Lord Jesus for Savior, come here to platform while the boys and girls sing."

The boys and girls went on to the platform. Heads bowed everywhere. Then there was soft singing, "Silent Night, Holy Night! All is calm, all is bright!"

There were footsteps coming to the platform. The song ended and the church was quiet. Quiet like the still just after sundown. Then the preaching man said, "Amen," and everyone raised his head and looked up.

Ramji looked right into the faces of Father and Mother

standing by the preaching man. *It can't be! It can't be Father and Mother!* Ramji was breathless. His mouth was open. He leaned forward, looking! Just looking!

Then Father smiled big. Mother smiled little, carefully watching Ramji. Ramji could not smile. He could not do anything! Then he did get his eyes to blink. *It is Father and Mother! They've found great God, Lord Jesus!*

Ramji felt his legs move. He rushed to Father and Mother. He leaned his head against Father.

"Your songs did it, son" Father said. "And the way you live after go to that school! We talk to teacher and she say our village have school just like it next year!"

Ramji put one arm around Father and one around Mother. No words were coming at all, and there were tears in his eyes. But his heart was singing. His whole heart was singing for joy to great God, Lord Jesus.

13. SOMETHING NEW FOR NARSING

Narsing stood in the middle of the mud hut that was his home in India. The boy, not quite thirteen wondered just where he could hide the extra kite string he held in his hands.

That brother Arun! I not share my string with him. I want my kite go higher than anybody's!

Narsing noticed the neat litttle piles of folded clothing on the floor along one wall. The poorer Hindu families had no furniture except *charopys*, low beds made of woven strings that were tied to the four legs.

I know! Narsing thought to himself walking to his clothes. *I hide string in own clothes. Arun not look here, ever!*

Narsing tucked every inch of the string inside his own folded clothes. The boy turned his head quickly one way, then another, watching carefully that nobody see.

With the string hid, Narsing turned and ran out of doors. Nearby, boys and girls were gathering under a tree. Narsing knew what that meant. The preaching man from another village had come and would tell stories and would show the boys and girls how to write. There was no school in the village, as Narsing's was one of the poorer Hindu villages.

Narsing stood still and watched the boys and girls come running toward the tree. *I know what man preaching about,* the boy thought to himself wriggling his right toes in the dust. *He talk every time about living God, Lord Jesus who save people from sin! He say we take this Jesus God into heart, then we go to heaven when die!*

When Narsing saw some of the boys motion for him to come, he looked the other way quickly. He was still thinking.

Preaching man say Jesus God want all of heart! He want hands for do good things—not bad anymore, not ever! Narsing

73

shrugged his shoulders. He thought of the kite string hid so well in his clothes. *This Jesus One want feet go only good places! Not bad places anymore, even once! He want lips say only good things!* Narsing looked toward the tree.

I want write, though, I go with boys and girls. I not very much listen only when man tell how write! This new god want whole person belong him, not like Hindu gods. Hindus have many gods, much different!

Hindus *do* have many gods! For Hinduism holds that God is in everything, in a million or more combinations. "As chemical elements exist in many combinations, just so with God," says the Hindu.

He may be present as a swan, as a book, as a rock. He may even be present as a cobra! If the Hindu feels in the mood to pray he may pray to just anything he sees. If he does not feel that anything he sees suits him to pray to, he can make himself a little mud god and pray to it just as well. So a Hindu's god may be called *Siva*. He may be called *Vishnu*. He may have the name *Rama* or *Hari,* or *Maruti!*

Siva had been the god of Narsing's family. As long as nothing very bad happened to the family, Siva kept on being the god. If trouble or sorrow were to come, the family might blame it onto Siva, and change to the worship of another god.

I like our god, Siva! Narsing thought, nearing the edge of the crowd of children. *He easy to please with little offering of rice and butter! If I bad, I take offering of beautiful marigolds so he not angry with me! That Siva, he very good god. I give a little sugar sometimes too. He treat Narsing very good, very good!*

Narsing stood behind the very last boy in the crowd around the preaching man. He heard the man say one boy or girl could come put some marks on the blackboard on his lap.

Then the man had every boy and girl sit down so all could see the blackboard. A boy from a village where there was a school had told Narsing they had a big blackboard on the wall of the school.

Narsing and the other boys and girls had often coaxed their fathers to get a school. But no one had quite enough money for food, even. So no one could do anything about a school!

In some of the nearby villages, even girls were getting to study sometimes. They did not go to the same school as the boys. For the boys studied how to do farming and helping fathers. Girls studied how to make a home and to do nursing.

Narsing heard the preaching man say, "I will tell a story!" The boy dug his toes into the dirt and pulled himself between two boys in front of him. The boys wiggled and made room for Narsing.

The man said, "This is a story of Mary. This mark on the blackboard means Mary." The man made a mark, and told the boys and girls to make a mark like it when they heard the word Mary in the story.

The boys and girls moved around so everyone would have a place to write in the dirt.

"This is also a story of an angel," the man said. "This mark is for angel. You make a mark for angel when you hear it!"

The man told more and more story and showed the boys and girls how to write words. He said, "Angel is beautiful creature which lives high in sky. Sometimes an angel comes to earth for people to see." Boys and girls were making marks as the man spoke slowly.

Good story! Narsing thought. *And I can make mark for Mary and angel, for beautiful and sky!*

The man spoke again, "Mary saw an angel. Mary saw the angel in her home." The man made a new mark for home.

Narsing's eyes grew wide with wonder. "Easy!" he said to the boy by his writing hand.

"Then angel said to Mary in her home," the man spoke very slowly now, 'Mary, you will be a mother!' "

Narsing like the mark for mother! *When I go home, I make*

mark to show my own mother! Then Narsing heard the man say, "Mary you will have a Son! His name will be called Jesus!" The man looked at the boys and girls. He showed them the mark to make for Jesus.

Jesus! Narsing made his mark slowly. He made it again and again. *That a beautiful name!* The boy whispered the name softly. *Like wind in trees when it make music,* he thought.

The preaching man stood up and leaned the blackboard against the tree trunk. Boys and girls stood up and moved around. Then a boy said to the preaching man, "Why you come from far away village, walking in hot sun to tell us story and show us how to write?"

The man smiled. He said kindly, "Because I know how write. Once I little boy too in mud village like yours. I then want so bad to write. I many times cry when I get in charopy at night because I cannot make marks—because I cannot read marks! I say to my father 'I want go to school!' But like your village, in my village no school."

Narsing thought as he watched and listened, *There almost tears in man's eyes. He know how to write, he come show us! He not want keep all he know to himself!*

Kites! String! Arun! The folded clothes! All came to Narsing's mind. He looked from the man to the ground. Some of the marks for Jesus were still plain in the dirt.

But my kite must go higher! It must go higher than Arun's! I older! I bigger! But Arun very good kite flyer!

Narsing turned from the preaching man without a word. Voices of the boys and girls still talking to him sounded in Narsing's ears as he followed the road toward his own little hut.

Then other sounds came from down the road. Shouting, and singing, it seemed! Narsing ran as fast as he could in that direction.

Ah, the Marharja, the prince of the province! On his royal elephant! Narsing stood still and watched. The boy's eyes were wide, and great happiness filled him inside. *I get to see the prince,* he said half out loud.

Narsing looked to see who all was gathering along the road to watch. There lay Jalam Singh, the poorest of all the beggars of the village. He too would get to see! He had only dirty rags on his brown, bony body. For months he had been in this same spot. Narsing remembered when first he saw the beggar there.

Today, as every day he held out his bowl to all who passed, hoping for a handful of rice.

The beating of the drums now was loud. More people were gathering and shouting. Many were walking along beside the royal elephant.

Maybe they walk on Jalam Singh! Narsing thought. He pushed a swallow down his dry throat.

No! People were moving around Jalam Singh! The royal elephant was almost at the beggar's side. The prince looked down as the long bony arm held out the bowl for some rice.

"What!" Narsing thought. *The prince is ordering procession stop!*

Sure enough, the elephant stood still. The prince dismounted and walked straight toward the beggar.

How handsome! Narsing thought, looking at the tall prince.

His bright yellow turban shone in the hot India sun. The tall bushy feather on it in front pointed straight to the sky.

Narsing's hands rubbed over his own short pants full of wrinkles as he looked at the prince's well pressed uniform.

The prince stopped in front of the beggar still holding out his bowl for rice.

"Beggar, give me some of your rice!" the ruler of the province commanded looking straight into the beggar's eyes.

Jalam Singh looked at the few grains in his bowl. Then lifting his sunburned eyes to the ruler he said, "But this is all rice I have!"

Narsing's heart was beating so loud he wondered if the

77

people next to him could hear it. He watched the prince! He watched the beggar!

"Give me some of your rice," the prince commanded again, without looking away from the beggar.

The beggar still held out the bowl. "But sir, I starve!" he said.

A third time the ruler said to the beggar, "Beggar give me some of your rice!"

Jalam Singh moved one hand slowly to the bowl and lifted out three little grains of rice. His eyes followed almost with hate, Narsing thought, the move of the ruler as he felt the rice drop into his own hand.

The prince looked at the rice carefully. He made a move with his arm for the people to clear the way, and he tossed the rice beyond the roadside.

Then the prince reached into his wallet and lifted out little gold nuggets that he dropped into the beggar's bowl, one, two, three!

The ruler turned back to his elephant, mounted and ordered the procession to move on.

Narsing stood motionless. *One, two, three!* he thought. Then he turned and started toward home. *Only as much as beggar willing to give! And tiny those nuggets, for beggar picked out tiniest grains!*

As Narsing neared home he glanced toward the tree where the preaching man and the boys and girls had been gathered. *The preaching man give very much,* Narsing thought. *He know how write! He come teach us all he know! That man share much, very much!*

"Share!" Narsing said the word out loud. Then the thought, *I ashamed. I not share with my brother my kite string!*

Narsing took a few steps slowly, thinking, and thinking. Then a smile crossed his face and he ran to his hut. He looked inside. No one was there. He moved quickly to his folded

78

clothes. He carefully pulled out all the string and edged over to Arun's pile of clothes.

Narsing's mouth was dry as he worked fast. He hid the last bit of string well in Arun's things. *Now I go tell Arun, "Surprise, surprise!"*

Narsing thought as he went to hunt Arun, *If I give Arun kite string, I know he go with me to hear preaching man. My heart tell me there much more to story of Jesus, and I want share story with Arun too!* Narsing felt good with the happy feeling that was inside him. *In heart, something new for Narsing,* he thought, *since preaching man come for tell stories and teach how to write!*

14. GREAT DAY FOR NANOY

Nanoy (Nan oy′) squeezed his eyes shut as other Filipinos in the crowded outrigger talked loudly of the boat being out of gas.

I not want to go to that island of Luzon anyway, the boy said to himself. *But when Father die and Mother all the time cry, cry, I have to go to Luzon with papers Mother say man there must have. Now coming home, out of gas in great Pacific! Maybe drift for hours and hours. Maybe get carried where no other boat find us!*

Nanoy opened his eyes for a quick look at the great waves of water in every direction. He pinched his eyes shut again and scooted down a little tighter between the people next to him. It was cold in the boat! Nanoy shivered!

And I wanted to go to field and make water from great irrigation ditch go on dry little rice plants. Then I could use Father's bolo (a long bladed knife) *to open ditch into our field.*

Nanoy pictured himself cutting branches off the nearby trees to put across the big ditch of water to make a dam. Then the water would run into Nanoy's tiny field, and water the plants.

When Nanoy used to go to the field with Father, Father would say, "Nanoy, some day you use bolo too!" Then, sometimes, Father would smile big at Nanoy and say, "And when you big enough to do full day's work, you even have bolo of own!"

Nanoy opened his eyes again and looked at the people in the boat. He wondered what they had all been to the island of Luzon for. He was glad he was not sitting next to the man huddled by the two Americans. The man was the native evangelist in Nanoy's village on the tiny island of Romblon, and he

80

had often asked Nanoy to come to the little white church where he preached.

Out of the corner of his eye, Nanoy watched the preacher talking to the Americans. *I not have anything to do with that that preacher and his church!* Nanoy thought. *I like gods of the hills and trees! I keep hid among others in boat so preacher not see me at all!*

As the boat rocked up and down over the waves, the preacher's voice sounded above the swish of the water. He was saying, "We are helpless out here in the boat on the great ocean. But we have a great God in heaven who can help us get to shore."

Nanoy turned his head enough to see the man speaking. *He mean what he say! I can tell by look on face!*

The preacher said again, "These Americans, Mr. and Mrs. Bill McKee are believers in the great living God, the Lord Jesus too. They are coming to our island to help us in our church."

O, now Americans in white church too! Nanoy thought.

Nanoy heard the man's voice again, "These people are going to pray to our God. Any of you who want to may pray, too!"

Bill and Sharon McKee prayed. The preacher prayed. While the preacher was still asking God to help them, many of the people began talking at once.

"Boat! Boat is coming!" Nanoy heard someone say.

"So far away it only looks like boat," someone else said hopelessly.

The preacher kept on praying. Nanoy listened. He watched the preacher and the Americans.

"Is a boat! Is a boat!" a man's voice boomed loud.

A larger outrigger was speeding through the water. *Is coming right at us!* Nanoy thought lifting his head high for a look.

Nanoy could not believe it, but there it was, coming closer and closer. No one could hear the preacher now. Everyone was talking.

The preacher put up his hand and the people in the boat became quiet. Then the preacher and the Americans each said a thankyou prayer to God for sending a boat to their rescue.

The larger boat pulled along side and men fastened the two boats together. Nanoy's heart was beating fast as he watched the men work. Nanoy watched closely the preacher and the Americans. *They not bad people,* he thought. *They even very good people maybe!* The boy said softly, "Little white church—"

Nanoy looked in the direction he thought Romblon lay. *With boat pulling us to shore, I soon get to field to use Father's bolo after all!* he thought.

Later, Nanoy stood with his mother in their own little hut. "I go fast now to field to turn water on rice plants?" he asked Mother.

"At thirteen you not very big to alone try watering, Nanoy!" Mother cried hard again.

Nanoy stood thinking. He felt himself swallowing and swallowing. He said tenderly, "Please not cry, Mother. I take Father's bolo and I go to field and do watering just like Father would do. You know Father used to say, 'Give Filipino bolo and he make a living!' Then Father would smile, remember Mother."

Nanoy watched Mother closely. "Father would tell us how Filipinos cut down great strong trees with bolos. And would cut bamboo for houses. How Filipinos cultivate soil, harvest crops, mend dikes and turn water on drying rice plants all with bolo, Mother! Just bolo!"

Mother walked slowly to a large chest in the corner and lifted out a long knife in a case.

Nanoy's breath almost quit coming. The boy held out his hands and took the bolo as Mother held it toward him. Thin brown fingers edged their way slowly over the leather case. Hands trembled as they held the bolo close to Nanoy's heart.

Nanoy quickly tied the string on it around his waist. "I go Mother! I go turn water on rice plants in field!" As Nanoy went out the door he thought, *If there no rice, there no eating!* The boy hurried toward the field.

At the field Nanoy looked down at the ditch of water. A small brown hand clutched the handle of the bolo and inched it tenderly from the case. He stopped and began digging a hole in the dike so the water could run into the field. The ground was dry and hard. Nanoy worked carefully. Water dripped from his forehead as he cut and as he dug grass and sod away from the hole. *Father do it! I do it too!* he thought as he worked.

Finally it seemed the hole must be big enough for the water to go through the field. But the water in the ditch was low and was running slowly.

Ah, I remember! Nanoy thought. *Father would cut branches and lay across the ditch a little way below the hole to stop the water and make it go fast-like through the hole into the field.*

Nanoy hurried to some nearby trees and quickly chopped off branches with Father's bolo. Back at the ditch with the branches, Nanoy pushed them across the ditch and chopped through them into the mud. *That stop fast water from going on down big ditch,* he decided.

More dirt and more dirt the boy piled against the branches until a high bank was piled up so the water began going through the hole.

"It very good!" the boy said out loud as the water started into the field.

Nanoy looked up from the plants as he heard someone call his name. There on the back of a big gray water buffalo rode Selmo, Nanoy's very best friend.

"Slide on!" Selmo called. "I go to grandfather's and very soon back!"

"To grandfather's!" Nanoy repeated, thinking how close grandfather lived and how quickly they could go on the fast moving buffalo. *It such fun to ride!* he thought.

Nanoy glanced at the water again. It seemed to be flowing smoothly through the hole into the field now. He started to slip the bolo into the case at his side. His hand tightened on the handle.

"Thanks Selmo!" Nanoy said. "I love ride! But today with Father's bolo I make water run onto dry rice plants."

Selmo smiled big at Nanoy, gave the buffalo a tap on the side with a little stick and rode off with a wave, toward grandfather's.

Nanoy wished Selmo had been walking. If he had he maybe would have stayed and talked with him. It was lonely here in the field by himself. But Nanoy kept on watching the water, and kept the grass and weeds out of the hole.

When he stood up from being down on his knees a long time, an old man came slowly walking toward him. The man said, "You doing watering alone, boy?"

Nanoy told of his father's death. He told how Mother cried all the time and was much of the time lying down ill.

The old man spoke slowly to Nanoy. "I know living God in heaven already help you. He help you do good job watering dry rice plants! Small boy do this good job only with good God helping!" The old man pointed over the field where the water was running smoothly, and shook his head kindly.

"Living God in heaven you say?" Nanoy asked him. "You know that great God others sometimes speak of to me?"

The old man squatted down on the ground and motioned for Nanoy to squat down beside him. His wrinkled old face shone in the late afternoon sun. He said, "Long time ago, so long I not know exact when, I go to market to buy eggs. When I at home I find eggs wrap in paper with printing on two sides." The man held his two hands together palms up, then turned them over quickly for Nanoy to see what he meant.

"I like much to read, so I read every word on papers! I read one side! I turn paper over and read other side!" The man held up his hands again, then turned them over once more quickly. "I read every word on paper wrap on every egg!"

Nanoy looked into the old man's eyes. They were kind looking eyes, and the man's voice was pleasant to listen to.

"Those wrap papers, boy, they talk to my heart about God. They say there sin in every man's heart. They say that God love man even with sin in heart, but God want man to have sin gone from heart. So God send own Son, Lord Jesus into world to be One to save people from that bad sin."

Nanoy could feel his mouth open wider and wider. His lips were dry. He wondered about the sin in his own heart.

The old man told more to Nanoy. He said he wanted so much to know more about this One who could save that he walked back to the village where he bought the eggs. He asked the men at the market if they knew where the papers had come from that were wrapped around the eggs. They told him the papers were from a book called the Bible that someone had given them. They did not like the book so they used the papers from it to wrap things in that they sold.

The old man said the market men told him where he could buy a Bible, so he bought one and took it home.

He read in the Bible how God loves all people. And how He sent His own Son, the Lord Jesus into the world to save all people from their sins.

The old man looked straight into Nanoy's eyes and added, "It say in Bible that if man accept Lord Jesus into heart, he is saved! Is right, too, that Bible!"

The old man looked into the lowering sun and slowly shook his head as he smiled and said, "I accept that Lord Jesus! My whole family accept Him! Many friends ask and we tell, and they too accept!"

Nanoy's heart was pounding in little jerks, it seemed. Something inside him wanted to hear more from the old man.

The old one said, "Family and friends pray together and sing songs in my house. Soon too small for all people. So out of

85

little rice money we bring some each time and build little church! See! Way there, little white church!"

"Little—white—church!" Nanoy could hardly get the words said.

"Must go on" the old man said standing unsteadily to his feet. "You think much, boy, about good living God and pretty soon you too accept Him as Savior!" The old man smiled, and walked away from the field.

Nanoy looked toward the setting sun. He looked then at the field, water running evenly through the rows of rice plants. He knew he could turn the water off now and go to his home, to Mother.

Once more a small brown hand clutched firmly the handle of the bolo. The bolo cut down through the mud and branches and opened the water again to go on through the big ditch. It closed up the hole into the field, and Nanoy was ready to go home.

The bolo was thrust gently into the case, and let drop at the boy's side.

Thoughts raced through Nanoy's mind as he hurried along the road. At his hut he pushed open the door and ran quickly to Mother. She was lying on her rattan bed. "The bolo did work well in the field, Mother! The water did run just like had Father been chopping the branches and cutting the hole!"

Mother sat on the edge of her bed.

"And Mother, two times this day have I heard of great living God in heaven, Lord Jesus. On the boat when we not have gas for engine, preacher prayed to Him. Two Americans with him pray too! And Mother, in field today old man came telling about same God."

Nanoy could feel his heart beating in those same little jerks again. He said, "This God loves everyone, Mother, everyone! I almost pray to Him in field when I start working on ditch. I very much wanted water to go on rice plants! Old man said good God did help me! He help everyone!"

"O, Nanoy, those good words you say," said Mother. "For today preacher and two Americans visit me. Americans here in our village to help in little white church, and are visit every person!" Mother did not even have tears in her eyes, Nanoy noticed.

Mother untied the string holding the bolo around Nanoy's waist. She said, "So water go well for Nanoy in field, using Father's bolo!"

Nanoy felt big, and he felt glad inside as he replied, "Water went well, Mother. Water is saving dry little rice plants!"

Mother laid the bolo in Nanoy's hands that were open in his lap. A smile came to her lips as she said, "You do man's work today, Nanoy! You now big enough to have bolo of own! This, today, your bolo!"

"O, thank you, Mother! Thank you!" The boy's hands shook and his voice sounded strange even to himself. He swallowed hard, trying to make some more words come. Finally he added, "This great day for Nanoy! Bolo of own! And on this day decide to go to white church!"

He looked at Mother, and the biggest happiness he ever knew came inside him. "And you go with me, Mother! You have smile now, big smile! You give me bolo, and you go with me white church!"

15. AMERICAN GIRL PILOTS FOR GOD

Betty Green lay on the lawn in front of her home at the edge of Seattle, Washington.

The day was just right for a girl, exactly fourteen, to be watching a plane in the sky. The sun was under a cloud enough of the time that Betty could watch the plane easily.

I wish I could sit in the pilot's seat! Betty daydreamed. *I could cross rivers and mountains. I could go from the east to the west. Why, I could even go from country to country!* Betty breathed faster and faster. "I could!" she said out loud.

From the time Betty's brother, Joseph, turned pilot, Betty could hardly keep her own feet on the ground. She listened to every word Joseph said about planes. She watched Joseph's face as he talked. She had him draw pictures for her and explain his every move as he took a big metal bird into the air.

As Betty watched the plane that day in front of her home, she sat up with a start. "I *can* be a pilot," she said. She snapped her right thumb and third finger in a loud pop. "Women are doctors now-a-days! They're scientists! And they're pilots, too! Of course I can be a pilot!"

Betty leaned her head way back as the plane came directly over her. *I'll be a regular bird, I will,* she thought. *I'll fly and I'll fly and I'll fly! I love the Lord, and maybe I can do more for Him in the air than I ever could do on the ground!* Betty squeezed her eyes shut and prayed, "Please guide me Lord to do just what I should!"

That summer slipped by very quickly. More summers slipped by quite like it, with Betty still thinking about planes. Then war broke out in many parts of the world.

When United States went into the war, Betty went as fast as she could to the office where she could join the Women's

Airforce Service Pilot division. For short, it was called WASP!

In the service, Betty's name stayed just plain Betty Green. The young women were treated as officers, but WASP gave no titles of rank.

But Betty did not care what she was called. For now she was off the ground most of the time. She was in the pilot's seat as she had wished for, years ago, as she lay on the ground and looked into the sky.

Soaring through the skies in the air target towing, Betty prayed, "While the war is on, Lord, please help me as I serve here. When peace comes again, please show me what you want me to do for You!"

When peace did come, Betty prayed again, and again, "I know there is a service each Christian should give, Lord. Please show me what mine should be!"

Each time Betty thought of her work, she felt sure that somehow it must have a plane in it. And as Betty would close her eyes to think and to pray, she would see herself in the pilot's seat.

"But," the flying young woman said to herself, "I can't just fly around in circles and say I'm doing it for the Lord! I must be really serving some place!"

Then God showed Betty Green exactly what she could do. Some other young people who were pilots during the war began thinking of air service for God, too. Then the wonderful God they all loved brought several of these people together. From the east coast and from the west, young people met and talked of distances they could quickly cover in planes.

With eyes wide, and words coming rapidly, one young man said, "In planes we can skim over jungles and mountains to mission stations in no time! And it takes weeks now to get to some of the places!"

"We can haul supplies as well as missionaries," another young pilot said quickly.

"Missionaries! Supplies!" Betty whispered to herself. The jungle swept under her right there in her chair!

So with that group of pilots, the Missionary Aviation Fellowship started early in 1945.

The minute the fellowship was ready for action, Betty was into the air. First she went south. She flew into and out of the jungle training camp for the Wycliff Translators near the Guatemalan border.

Below her plane, near-naked brown natives jostled along in oxcarts. Some natives rode little brown burros. Others trudged on foot up steep mountain passes and over winding paths into adobe villages.

As Betty looked down into Guatemala, she knew she was looking into the second largest, and the most densely populated country in all of Central America. As she looked, Betty prayed, "Please Lord, help us win many, many of these dear souls to Thee."

Below, somewhere in the jungles was the Mayan Monument discovered in recent years. "They say it has been standing there for a thousand years or more." Betty talked to herself as she flew. "And it has words on it that were very meaningful to the natives who built it!" Betty looked down as though looking right at it. Then she glanced at the little Bible in the cockpit beside her. "But here are words that are eternal!" she said into the world all around her.

Betty thought of the natives who so long have lived in Guatemala. "Over half the population of the country are pure blood Indians. And of all the Indians of North America, and maybe even of South America too, those of Guatemala have stayed more nearly like the very first Indians ever known of!"

"O, if only they could read and write well, how it would help!" Betty talked to herself again. But over three-fourths of the people who are over seven years old cannot read or write one word!"

Betty glanced again at the little black Book beside her. She said out loud, "The entrance of thy words giveth light" (Psalm 119:130). "There is hope for these people of Guatemala!"

Betty's next work took her into Peru, South America. Here Betty Green was the first woman pilot to fly the Peruvian Andes. Again the plane flew in workers and materials for Wycliff Translators.

In the air as the plane roared over Lake Titicaca, bordering Peru and Bolivia, Betty looked down on the highest large body of water in the world used for any shipping. It is 12,507 feet high.

"Water! Boats! Everything moving along so slowly it takes ages to get any place," Betty whispered to herself. She prayed there in the cockpit, "Thank You Lord, for helping men get faster ways of moving around. Now the Word can reach these dear people so much more quickly!"

Then a lump came to Betty's throat as she said, "Teachers! How they need teachers! For as in Guatmala, over half of the people old enough to go to school can't read or write one word!"

Betty looked down on the great land below her. She prayed again that God would get His message of salvation through the thick tangle of forests that cover much over half of the entire country.

As the plane roared over the Andes, Betty looked down at some of the dome-shaped mountains. The highway twisted up, around, and over. Betty said as she looked, "Seems as if a narrow ribbon had just been dropped, and turned into a narrow road right where it landed.

Betty's heart was happy that she was able to serve the Lord in such a needy country. But another country on the other side of the world had needy people too. And as Betty had daydreamed when she was a girl, there were oceans to cross. Betty crossed some, and went next to Africa.

There too, people needed the gospel! Black-skinned people, these were! So Betty was loaned to the Sudan Interior Mission for work in Nigeria, and bordering parts of French West Africa.

She was the first woman to get permission to fly in the Sudan. And it took government cabinet action to get that permission!

Here Betty piloted missionaries into and out of their stations. The silver streak in the sky was serving as defense against sin while below something different was in action. There on the ground, eleven hundred camel corpsmen helped in national defense!

Again Betty shuddered that so few of the natives could read or write. She shuddered even more that so few had any knowledge of the Lord Jesus.

One day as she looked down onto the ground slipping by rapidly under her, she said to herself, "And to think that in the first few hundred years after the birth of Christ, there were strong Christian kingdoms in some of these places!" Betty wrinkled her forehead, then added, "It proves that we must be faithful to the word of God and guard the right to have it taught to keep it powerful in our lands!"

Betty kept doing her best to keep the Word powerful every way that she could. In 1952 she came to her own homeland and worked for three years in the MAF office. But Africa called again! This time Betty was loaned to the sister organization, British Missionary Aviation Fellowship.

This second time in Africa Betty went to the Republic of Sudan, south of Egypt, west of Ethiopia. There, based in a place which was convenient to all five mission stations working in that country Betty had many thrilling experiences.

There was the day little Loraine Conwell was playing outdoors on one of the isolated Sudan United Mission Stations.

Loraine was dressed for the African drizzle that was falling. She was having fun in the mud. But she was having more fun eating peanuts. Then the little girl tried to cough. She tried to swallow. Loraine could not cough! She could not swallow! A peanut was caught in her windpipe.

"She's strangling!" a passerby screamed. "Little girl strangling!"

Someone ran with the girl to the nurses at the mission building. The nurses worked hard as they could. As they worked, Roy Conwell, the father helped! He looked at the little girl choking! "The hospital," he said feebly. "Nine days away by tractor through the mud! The nearest phone thirty miles!"

The man looked at his little daughter once more. He dashed from the room and ran to the tractor. By late afternoon he reached the phone, and a call went through to the MAF base.

Before dawn, Betty Green set the plane down at the little outpost station. Loraine, her father and a nurse were soon in the air with Betty. As the moments clicked by they neared Khartoum. Landing there, the child was soon in the hospital.

The chest specialist operated. Loraine began breathing easily. Betty Green stood by to wing the three back to the tiny mission station.

Before leaving, the little girl squeezed the warm hand of the doctor. He looked down into her wide open eyes and said, "It's a good thing you came when you did, young lady! Tomorrow I'm leaving for England!"

Into the plane, into the skies, and down again at the mission, the pilot and passengers timed themselves since their departure "Exactly thirty-two hours we have been away!" said the father. "What would the cause of missions do without you MAFers and God?"

Betty smiled. She smiled because her heart was happy that God was using her in His great work.

Betty Green continues to smile as God continues to use her. Her right-hand thumb and third finger snap once in a while too. With each little pop, Betty Green says, "I'll fly and I'll fly and I'll fly! Maybe I can do greater things in the air for God than I ever could do on the ground!"

16. A BOY AND THE WORD IN VENEZUELA

In late afternoon Tomas (To mas´) stood at the edge of the twisty Orinoco river in Venezuela watching the sailboats ply through the water. The tall thin boy of thirteen was thinking about the white man T. J. Bach who had come to the Indian's jungles many months before.

Every day this white man was teaching and preaching a message. It was a message new to the Indians. For it was about a living God in heaven who gave His Son, the Lord Jesus to be the Savior from sins to any who believe in Him and trust Him.

My father, first Indian to trust! Tomas thought watching the sails lean with the wind. *He so faithful to word in little Book Mr. Bach call Bible, he become kind father! Happy father even! Now Mother and I trust same good Lord Jesus!*

A warm satisfied feeling flowed all around inside Tomas. He thought how good it was to have his sins forgiven and to have a Friend always near, as the Lord Jesus was with him now.

But my best friend Arme, (Ar me´) *he not come to hear Mr. Bach, not ever!* Tomas wrinkled his forehead. *He not even go near mission place. He go wide circle, way around place of Mr. Bach! I wish I so faithful to word in black Book that some way I show Arme true Lord Jesus!*

Tomas turned with a quick step. He looked straight into the eyes of Arme!

Tomas gasped. "I— I—"

Arme's eyes were big with excitement. "I come for you. I decide to go hunt for feathers of quetzal bird! I want that you go with me!"

"Feathers of quetzal bird!" Tomas could feel his own eyes open wide. He swallowed a hard lump of something in his throat. Tomas knew the quetzal was the bird sacred to the ancient Indians. He knew that some of the village Indians still used the hard-to-find feathers in some of their secret rituals. But Tomas and his family were taking no part in those certain things anymore.

Feelings on the inside of Tomas now seemed to be going all directions. He thought, *Arme not come to hear Mr. Bach, maybe Mr. Bach go with us! But, maybe Mr. Bach not think right to go hunt quetzal feathers!*

Tomas said gently, "That Mr. Bach very good hunter! He maybe find just right feathers. We take white man too?"

Arme looked back at Tomas with cold, staring eyes. "No!" he said firmly. "White man touch feathers, no good for Indians! We go! You, Arme, go!"

Tomas looked at the quiver of darts that lay across Arme's coppery back. A long slender blowgun was in the boy's hands.

"You *kill* quetzal?" Tomas asked, the flesh on the back of his neck quivering.

"No! No, no!" Arme answered quickly. "You know that bring very bad evil! You know, even if you not listen to Indian sayings anymore, but go now to hear white man's much talking!" Arme slid a hand back and forth on the blowgun. "We only get quetzal fathers. But we kill game, maybe."

Arme explained they could go up the river in his canoe. Then they could go into the jungles away from any villages. There the bird might be found. The boys could be gone overnight, and hunt and hunt!

Born and raised in the jungle lands, nothing was more exciting for Tomas than the twang of the Indian bow-cord and the hum of the arrow. The straight black hair standing from the boy's head in every direction seemed almost shaking.

But Tomas did want to do what the white teacher would say was right. He trusted the teacher-man since Father had become such a changed Father. And since he himself had such joy in his heart knowing Jesus.

Tomas smiled at Arme. Arme had always been his friend, the two had grown up together. Even after Tomas accepted the new Jesus way, the boys were too fond of each other to be long apart. "I make plans for go, Arme! Sun soon go down now. We start first thing in morning?"

"In morning we go!" Arme answered. "I have boat ready!" The shorter boy turned and went toward his own mud hut.

Tomas glanced again at the sails above the water, and left on the trot for Mr. Bach's place.

Inside the mission building, Tomas told Mr. Bach of the plans the two boys had made. Tomas knew Father and Mother would want him to do what the white teacher said would be right. Hunting quetzal feathers was something that had not been discussed since the family had become Christians.

The teacher spoke slowly and looked straight at Tomas as he talked. "You want to be faithful to the Word of God, and still you want to hunt feathers for the Indians who do not know God!"

Tomas wiggled his toes on the wooden floor. "I do want be faithful to Word!" The boy knew how he felt, but did not know exactly how to explain it. "I not big care to hunt feathers, I rather just hunt and hunt! But Arme want to get feathers! Maybe if I go, there is way to show and to tell him of Lord Jesus!" Tomas wished Mr. Bach could look right inside his heart and see how much he wanted Arme to have the same God that he now had.

Mr. Bach looked very thoughtful. He opened his mouth as if to say something, then cleared his throat instead. A soft, extra-kind look came into his eyes. And Tomas thought sure it was a tear the man brushed away quicklike with the back of his hand.

Mr. Bach looked far, far away. Tomas stood motionless. All of a sudden the room was too silent. It was like the jungle when even one twig cracking, thunders through the trees.

When Mr. Bach spoke, his first words sounded strange.

96

"Tomas, I will tell you something!" The man sat down and motioned for Tomas to sit. Then the place seemed to be the mission place once more. Tomas listened closely.

Mr. Bach said, "When I was a young man, just a few years older than you are, I lived in a far away country, Denmark. I was studying very hard doing a kind of reading and writing that you do not yet know about. I was studying to be what is called an engineer."

Engineer! Tomas thought. *He maybe study all day and study all night to be thing called engineer!*

The man spoke again. Now his voice was like music of gentle water on the rocks in the river. "One day I was walking home from my classes. Another young man walking toward me held out a little piece of paper to me and said, "Will you please take this little tract? It has a message for you!"

Mr. Bach brushed an eye quickly again and said, "I was very unkind to the other young man. I yelled loudly at him in anger, "Why do you bother people with such reading? I will take care of my own interests!"

Tomas twisted his head to one side a little, watching Mr. Bach more closely than ever. *He never talk angry that way in this village, never!*

Then Tomas heard the man's words again. "But you know Tomas, that other young man did not return angry words to me! He didn't say one word. He just closed his eyes—and there on the busy street he folded his hands and his lips moved as if he were praying!"

A quick thought flashed through Tomas' mind. *That other boy want Mr. Bach trust in Lord Jesus like I want Arme!*

Mr. Bach said, "I saw tears pour from the other boy's eyes. I didn't have tears. I had only a crumpled and torn paper in my hand. I had ripped the tract into pieces the moment I got it into my hands!"

He was angry! For sure, very angry! Tomas thought.

"I walked quickly to my room," the man added. "Something

97

in my heart was not at peace. I was ashamed of the way I had acted. I felt the other boy's kindness pricking me all over!"

Tomas looked closely at Mr. Bach. *This the man now that come to our village. Kind white man, tender in heart!*

The man said, "I pasted the pieces of paper together and I read every word on the pasted up tract. The next thing I knew I was on my knees asking God's forgiveness of sin and asking for grace to accept the Lord Jesus as my Savior."

Tomas could see tears in Mr. Bach's eyes now, too many to brush off with the back of his hand. They splashed down onto his shirt already wet from the heat of the scorching Venezuela sun.

Mr. Bach added, "I trusted right then in the wonderful Lord Jesus. I was so happy to have Him in my heart that later I began giving out tracts to help other people come to know Him as I did. I never did anything else that made me so happy as helping others come to know Him!"

"I know, Mr. Bach! My heart is same way for Arme! I sometimes even have tears for him to know living Lord Jesus too!"

"You are right to have tears for Arme," Mr. Bach replied. "You are right, I feel, to go with him to hunt for the quetzal feathers. Let's pray that you have the very right way to tell him and show him his need."

The two prayed earnestly about the boy's trip, and Tomas thought, *I glad Mr. Bach did see right into my heart that I very big want to win Arme to Savior!"*

Tomas left the mission building and was breathless as he ran toward home to talk to Father and Mother. Burros were ambling up the steep cobbled streets, Indians walking beside them. Tomas sped past them. Heat-lightning flared over the jungle just outside the village. Thin rooting pigs grunted, and cringing dogs wallowed in the dust as Tomas ran.

In his own hut, Tomas told Father and Mother what he and Arme wanted to do, and all that Mr. Bach had said to him.

"You big now," Father said. "You travel in jungle and on river all life. You go! You special watch though, in gorge where rapids go down, down, between rock straight up like high walls!" Father motioned the *down* with his big rough brown hands. He held his palms open close together raising them higher and higher for the rock walls. Mother just looked.

Next morning as stars blinked from sight, and mist over the jungle began tinging with pink, the two boys paddled their canoe through the water. Tomas liked the feel of the jungle. He knew it lay in a great wavy mass each side of the river as far as he could even imagine.

Tomas looked up. Something dead, possibly, lay not too far east of the river for a ring of vultures was lowering, lowering. Not even a move of a wing could the boy see. But the birds glided down, and were then out of sight.

As day came on the sun blazed without mercy. The river twisted and swirled around dozens of little islands. On the sandpits crocodiles lay without movement except the flick of an eyelid.

Past the islands, the water began churning and splashing. It foamed up like an angry fountain. Tomas could feel his heart begin pounding. "The rapids, Arme! We take special care! See—great gorge far there, where rapids go down, down!" Tomas pointed with the hand that he ate with.

Arme dipped his paddle into the water and gave a big pull on the handle. He dipped on the wrong side and it swung the boat toward the rapids.

Tomas almost yelled, "Crazy! Why you do such thing?" Then he remembered Mr. Bach teaching from the Word, "The tongue of the wise useth knowledge aright..." (Proverbs 15:2). The swift thought hit him, *That why I come on trip, to use knowledge right!*

Tomas pushed on his paddle. He pulled. He paddled. He pulled harder than he ever had in all of his life. He saw Arme dipping hard and fast. *He know his mistake!* Tomas thought.

99

"Living God help us, please help us!" he prayed, forgetting about anything but God and His great power. Tomas saw Arme flash a look back at him. Arme stood in the front, Tomas tall like a tree, in the back.

Overhead, in the trees near the water, a clamor of hornbills seemed to say the birds sensed the danger. Tomas breathed quick, little short breaths. His arm muscles ached. "Please, great living Lord Jesus!" he prayed again.

The canoe sped out of the pull of the rapids. Something flapped in the air near Tomas' head. He brushed at it with his hand then sneaked a look as soon as he dared glance up from the water. A butterfly, big as a bird bounced up and down in the air. Tomas thought to himself, *Now God show us He not only guide past rapids, He also make beautiful creatures for man to look on!*

The canoe slid along now with easy paddling. The boys could talk. This was fun! They knew of a jungle clearing a few hours away and planned to sleep there.

The two paddled along as the river coiled and uncoiled, leading endlessly on into the mass of green jungle stillness. Tomas said, "For sure, Arme, God to make great living jungle must be great living God!"

Just then a thick cloud of flies settled about them. Each boy shooed with his hands and blew with his breath. Arme finally could talk through the whirr of the wings. "Very living God to make this much flies, if living at all, Tomas!"

Tomas felt a smile almost come onto his face. But the feeling slipped away quickly. He held a hand out, and rubbed his fingers together. "Strange hot, Arme! Feel!"

As he spoke, the sky turned into an angry looking dark cloud-race. Water dropped from the heavens in torrents. Quick, like a wild beast, a storm struck. The river turned black as it hissed and boiled. Tomas looked over the jungle. Great clouds of steam were arising. They hid even the tallest tree-

100

tops. They rolled like smoke-coils as the cold rain hit the hot jungle floor.

"Mean, this old storm is!" Arme yelled back to Tomas. The boys were paddling hard again to keep the boat on its course.

Then as quickly as it had struck, the storm stopped. Tomas said hurriedly but gently, "We say a verse over and over one day from our new Book, the Bible, '... He hath done all things well . . .' (Mark 7:37). Maybe we see not even the storm mean," said Tomas to Arme.

The boys were near to the clearing, and in a little while edged their canoe along shore. Arme gave a quick, high jump from the boat. His feet hit the mud on the river's edge, and one leg gave a twist. The boy screamed. "My ankle! I twist my ankle, Tomas!"

Tomas gasped. There had been a time when he would have called in great anger, "Clumsy! Clumsy! Why you get hurt way out here?" But he had learned that the Word of God said to be slow to anger.

Tomas jumped and landed near Arme. Tomas tried to help the other boy stand, but the ground was steep and it was slippery. He squatted down back of the shorter boy and put his hands under his armpits. He dug his toes deep into the mud and edged his way backward. He pulled Arme up to flat higher ground and there made a bed for the night. The jungle floor of the clearing was a deep mass of moss. So with only a little hollowing out, a bed was made for the injured boy.

"I sorry, Arme, Mr. Bach not here with us. You remember how he fix sprain on Jodar (Jo' dar)?"

Arme's face was tense and drawn. He said, "I laugh at your God about flies, Tomas! But you suppose He hear if we ask for help for hurt leg?"

Tomas' heart gave a happy thump. Even with Arme suffering, Tomas felt something inside him saying, *Thank you, thank you Lord Jesus!* His voice was shaky as he answered, "Of course He hear about hurt leg, Arme. The living God listen about everything! He like best of all to hear people say they want Him for Savior, to forgive sin in heart. But He help everybody! He not good only to people who love Him, Arme!"

Tomas heard words tumbling from his own lips. He heard himself telling Arme all he had hoped for so long to tell him. He felt his eyes close as he prayed for help to get his friend home.

Arme listened. Tomas felt his friend watching him closely. Arme said slowly, "We see what white man's God do for hurt leg!"

Tomas brought up some food from the canoe. As the boys ate, spider monkeys raced through the treetops scolding them for being in their part of the jungle. A white crane rose from rocks in the river, flapping heavy wings to get into the air. A flock of toucans with orange and red bills as long as Tomas' arm, screeched and screamed.

Then darkness came. Tomas said, "We pray again before we go sleep. We pray about help some way for leg. We pray that fire going all night keep fierce animals plenty far back in jungle." So the boy prayed aloud. He prayed for Arme and his hurt leg. He described the fierce animals to God as if He had never known of them before. He prayed that he would be faithful to the Word so that he could show forth God's love.

When he finished, Arme said thoughtfully, "You different boy all right Tomas, than before you trust Jesus God! Then you not very much care if anybody else hurt! Remember Tomas?"

Tomas felt his neck and his face flush warm. He was glad it was dark now. He answered softly, *"I remember, Arme. I so much remember, my heart hurts me! My heart not good then! I never real happy! No one happy at my home then!* Tomas shooed a mosquito. *Father very much not happy! Mother almost so much not happy! Then we find great living God, Lord Jesus, and everybody happy!*

"We sleep now, Tomas, we sleep?" Arme's voice sounded

102

as if he did not want to hear Tomas speak anymore.

Tomas thought, *I keep big blaze till bright daylight!*

Then came the night silence of the jungle. It was a silence Tomas never had liked. It was death-like, like the soundless coil of the poisonous snake! It was like the last instant before the fierce animal pounced! Then mosquitoes buzzed thick out of nowhere. Mosquitoes, millions of them, and bats swooping, darting, devouring mosquitoes! Then millions and millions more of the insects! And bats and bats and bats for more eating!

Then loud howls filled the air. The *areguato,* howler-monkeys had tuned up for the night, and theirs was a cry of wild rage and anger. One thing, Tomas thought to himself, *"Mosquitoes and bats gone now! Just gone!*

Tomas tried hard not to hear the monkey's loud howls. He blinked his eyes in the blackness. He thought of all that had happened since he stood only yesterday watching the sailboats, thinking of Arme.

Then his eyes blinked rapidly. His heart beat loud. He put his hands quickly on his chest. *I not want Arme hear loud pounding! But I not have to go now to hunt quetzal feathers! And I already get to tell Arme much about living God!*

Tomas felt himself shaking. He quietly tossed some more moss and sticks on the fire. He thought to himself over and over, *You so good, God in heaven! Thank you, O, thank you!*

When daylight came Tomas helped Arme into the canoe. They had come upstream into the jungle, so they glided rapidly downstream toward home.

As they came into the cove of their own little mud village, a canoe was just starting downstream. Tomas looked quickly a second time. He called loudly, "Mr. Bach! Stay! Ohhh, Mr. Bach!"

The man in the canoe looked back. The boat went ahead. Then the boat turned, and came swiftly back to the boys.

Tomas called again as the man neared. "Arme sprain ankle! Very bad hurt! You fix?"

103

Mr. Bach and the boys pulled their boats to the shore. The man jumped out and reached down for Arme. He carried the boy to the mission house, and tenderly worked with the leg.

Arme looked up into the man's face. Words came from his lips in short jerks. "You almost not here when we come!"

The man answered, "That's right! I knew I must get to the next village. They have been asking and asking for the Jesus story there too!"

Arme said very softly, "I not ever ask to hear! I even not want to listen when Tomas try tell me!"

The boy looked at Tomas and added, "But now I listen! Many reasons, I listen!" Arme looked again at the man. "Because Tomas not angry with me when I shoot canoe toward rapids! He only pull, work hard, work hard and help bring boat right again!"

The boy bit his teeth together hard as the man worked more. No sound came from him though except more words, "He not mad about *storm!* He even say verse to me about great God do all things well! And when I sprain ankle, he help me and all night keep bright fire going."

Arme swallowed, Tomas could see his throat too. He bent his head to listen well. Arme was talking again, "Best of all, he tell me about living Lord Jesus who makes heart clean from sin and help make ankle get well!"

Tomas looked at Mr. Bach. The boy felt tears in his own eyes and he saw Mr. Bach wipe an eye again with the back of his hand.

Inside Tomas was a thankyou to God for helping him live the Word, and to tell it to his very best friend. Tomas smiled and said, "I have Arme sit by me now in every service, Mr. Bach. And that Arme, he will be one to tell somebody else quick about living Lord Jesus!"